Study Guide for

Understanding Statistics

third
edition

Study Guide for

Understanding Statistics

third
edition

by William Mendenhall and Lyman Ott

prepared by

Barbara M. Beaver
Robert J. Beaver
University of California, Riverside

Duxbury Press
A division of Wadsworth, Inc.
North Scituate, Massachusetts

Duxbury Press
A Division of Wadsworth, Inc.

Printed in the United States of America
1 2 3 4 5 6 7 8 9 -- 84 83 82 81 80

Contents

PREFACE

1   WHAT IS STATISTICS?   1

    1.1   What Is Statistics?   1
    1.2   The Job of a Statistician   2

2   HOW TO PHRASE AN INFERENCE:
    GRAPHICAL METHODS   5

    2.1   Introduction   5
    2.2   Circle Charts   5
    2.3   Bar Charts   7
         Self-Correcting Exercises 2A   9
    2.4   Frequency Histograms and Frequency Polygons   10
         Self-Correcting Exercises 2B   14
         Exercises   15

3   HOW TO PHRASE AN INFERENCE:
    NUMERICAL METHODS   19

    3.1   Introduction   19
    3.2   Measures of Central Tendency   19
    3.3   Measures of Variability   22
         Self-Correcting Exercises 3A   25
    3.4   On the Practical Significance of the Standard
         Deviation   26
    3.5   A Short Method for Calculating the Variance and
         Standard Deviation   27
         Self-Correcting Exercises 3B   29
    3.6   How to Guess the Standard Deviation of Sample Data   30
         Exercises   31

4 PROBABILITY AND PROBABILITY
   DISTRIBUTIONS 35

   4.1 Introduction 35
   4.2 What Is Probability? 35
   4.3 Additivity of Probabilities 37
   4.4 Conditional Probability and Independence 40
   4.5 Random Variables 42
   4.6 The Binomial Probability Distribution 44
        Self-Correcting Exercises 4A 49
   4.7 The Normal Probability Distribution 50
        Self-Correcting Exercises 4B 56
        Summary 58
        Exercises 59

5 SAMPLING DISTRIBUTIONS 63

   5.1 Introduction 63
   5.2 Random Sampling 63
        Self-Correcting Exercises 5A 66
   5.3 The Central Limit Theorem and the Sampling
        Distribution of a Sample Mean 66
        Self-Correcting Exercises 5B 69
   5.4 The Sampling Distribution of a Sample Proportion 69
        Self-Correcting Exercises 5C 75
        Exercises 75

6 MAKING INFERENCES:
   ESTIMATION 77

   6.1 Introduction 77
   6.2 Point Estimation 79
        Self-Correcting Exercises 6A 82
   6.3 Interval Estimation 82
        Self-Correcting Exercises 6B 85
   6.4 Summary 85
        Exercises 86

7 MAKING INFERENCES: TESTING
   HYPOTHESES 89

   7.1 Introduction 89
   7.2 A Statistical Test of an Hypothesis 89

7.3   A Large-Sample Test of an Hypothesis   93
Self-Correcting Exercises 7A   98
7.4   The Level of Significance of a Statistical Test   99
Self-Correcting Exercises 7B   102
Exercises   102

8   COMPARISONS   105

8.1   Introduction   105
8.2   The Sampling Distribution of the Difference Between Two Sample Statistics   106
8.3   Estimation   108
Self-Correcting Exercises 8A   111
8.4   A Large-Sample Test of an Hypothesis   112
Self-Correcting Exercises 8B   116
Exercises   117

9   INFERENCES BASED ON SMALL SAMPLES   119

9.1   Introduction   119
9.2   Student's t Distribution   119
9.3   Small-Sample Inferences Concerning a Population Mean   123
Self-Correcting Exercises 9A   125
9.4   Small-Sample Inferences Concerning the Difference Between Two Means $(\mu_1 - \mu_2)$ 126
Self-Correcting Exercises 9B   130
9.5   Summary   130
Exercises   131

10   REGRESSION AND CORRELATION   133

10.1   Introduction   133
10.2   Scatter Diagrams and the Freehand Regression Line   135
10.3   Method of Least Squares   137
Self-Correcting Exercises 10A   141
10.4   Inferences Concerning the Slope of the Line, β_1 142
Self-Correcting Exercises 10B   146
10.5   The Coefficient of Linear Correlation   147
Self-Correcting Exercises 10C   152
10.6   Multiple Regression   152
Exercises   154

11 THE DESIGN OF AN EXPERIMENT: GETTING MORE FOR YOUR MONEY 159

11.1 Introduction 159
11.2 The Paired-Difference Experiment: An Example of a Designed Experiment 160
   Self-Correcting Exercises 11A 163
11.3 Choosing the Sample Size to Estimate μ or p 165
   Self-Correcting Exercises 11B 168
   Exercises 169

12 TESTING THE EQUALITY OF POPULATION VARIANCES 171

12.1 Introduction 171
12.2 A Test of an Hypothesis Concerning Two Population Variances 172
   Exercises 176

13 ANALYSIS OF VARIANCE 179

13.1 Introduction 179
13.2 The Logic Behind an Analysis of Variance 179
13.3 A Test of an Hypothesis Concerning More Than Two Population Means: An Example of an Analysis of Variance 181
   Self-Correcting Exercises 13A 187
13.4 Summary 188
   Exercises 189

14 CONTINGENCY TABLES 193

14.1 Introduction 193
14.2 Contingency Tables: A Test for Determining Whether Two Methods of Classification Are Independent 193
   Self-Correcting Exercises 14A 200
   Exercises 200

15 NONPARAMETRIC STATISTICS 203

15.1 Introduction 203
15.2 The Sign Test for Comparing Two Populations 204
   Self-Correcting Exercises 15A 207

15.3   Wilcoxon's Signed-Rank Test   208
       Self-Correcting Exercises 15B   210
15.4   Wilcoxon's Rank-Sum Test   211
       Self-Correcting Exercises 15C   214
15.5   Spearman's Rank Correlation Coefficient   215
       Self-Correcting Exercises 15D   220
       Exercises   221

SOLUTIONS TO SELF-CORRECTING EXERCISES   225

ANSWERS TO EXERCISES   255

Preface

The study of statistics differs from the study of many other college subjects. One must not only absorb a set of basic concepts and applications but must precede this with the acquisition of a new language.

We think with words. Hence, understanding the meanings of words employed in the study of a subject is an essential prerequisite to the mastery of concepts. In many fields, this poses no difficulty. Often, terms encountered in the physical, social, and biological sciences have been met in the curricula of the public schools, in the news media, in periodicals, and in everyday conversation. In contrast, few students encounter the language of probability and statistical inference before embarking on an introductory college-level study of the subject. Many consider the memorization of definitions, theorems, and the systematic sequence of steps necessary for the solution of problems to be unnecessary. Others are oblivious to the need. The consequences for both types of students are disorganization and disappointing achievement in the course.

This study guide attempts to lead you through the language and concepts necessary for a mastery of the material in *Understanding Statistics, Third Edition* by William Mendenhall and Lyman Ott (Duxbury, 1980).

A study guide with answers is intended to be an individual student study aid. The subject matter is presented in an organized manner that incorporates continuity with repetition. Most chapters bear the same titles and order as the textbook chapters. Within each chapter, the material both summarizes and reexplains the essential material from the corresponding textbook chapter. This allows you to gain more than one perspective on each topic and, we hope, enhances your understanding of the material.

At appropriate points in each chapter, you will encounter a set of Self-Correcting Exercises in which problems relating to new material are presented. Terse, stepwise solutions to these problems are found at the back of the study guide. You can refer to these at any intermediate point in the solution of each problem or use them as a stepwise check on any final answer. The Self-Correcting Exercises not only provide the answers to specific problems but also reinforce the stepwise logic required to arrive at a correct solution to each problem.

At the end of each chapter, additional sets of exercises can be found. These exercises are provided for the students who feel that further individual practice is needed in solving the kinds of problems found within each chapter. At this point, having been given stepwise solutions to the Self-Correcting Exercises, you are now presented with only final answers to problems. When your answer disagrees with that given in the study guide, you should be able to find your error by recalculating and comparing your solution with the solutions to similar Self-Correcting Exercises. If the answer given disagrees with yours only in decimal accuracy, it can be assumed that this difference is due only to rounding error at various stages in the calculations.

When the study guide is used as a supplement, the textbook chapter should be read first. Then you should study the corresponding chapter within the study guide. Key words, phrases, and numerical computations have been left blank so that you can insert a response. The answers are presented in the page margins. These should be covered until you have supplied a response for each blank. Bear in mind, though, that in some instances more than one answer is appropriate for a given blank. It is left to you to determine whether your answer is synonymous with the answer given within the margin.

Since perfection is something to be desired, we ask that the student who has located an error kindly bring it to our attention.

Barbara M. Beaver
Robert J. Beaver

Chapter 1

WHAT IS STATISTICS?

1.1 What Is Statistics?

Statistics involves sampling from a larger body of data called a _____.   population
Consider the following examples of statistical problems.

1. The opinions of stockholders in a large corporation are of interest to the board of directors of the corporation. Rather than poll the entire set of stockholders, questionnaires are sent only to a selected group.
2. An experiment is conducted to assess the effect of a shock stimulant on the time to completion of a specified task for laboratory rats. Ten rats are selected and subjected to the shock treatment and their completion times are recorded.

The following characteristics are common to both of these statistical problems.

   a. The measurements or observations obtained cannot be predicted in advance.
   b. A sample is taken from a larger body of data.
   c. From each element in the sample, one or more measurements or pieces of data are collected.
   d. It is assumed that the conclusions drawn from the study apply to more than those elements within the sample. For example, opinions of all stock-holders would comprise the larger set of measurements of interest to the experimenter. This larger set of measurements is called a population.

A population can exist conceptually or it can exist in fact. In example 2, given above, the measurements constitute a _____ population of measure-   conceptual
ments made on rats placed in the same experimental situation. On the other hand, consider the problem of estimating the proportion of stockholders of a particular corporation who are in favor of a certain proposal. Here, each voting stockholder in favor of the proposal could be counted as a "1," and those opposed or

population

sample

actual

sample
conceptual

inferences

having no opinion as a "0." For this problem, the _____ consists of a set of ones and zeros associated with the stockholders in the corporation.

A _____ is a subset of measurements selected from the population.

1. One hundred voting residents, chosen as a cross-section of a given city, were polled regarding their opinion about the new city bond issue. These 100 people represent a sample from the (actual, conceptual) population of voting residents of that city.

2. Examination scores are recorded for 50 students who have been taught using a certain experimental method. These scores represent a _____ from a(n) (actual, conceptual) population consisting of the large number of measurements that might have been obtained from other students placed under similar conditions.

Statistics is concerned with a theory of information and its application in making inferences based on sample information about populations in the sciences and industry. The objective of statistics is to make _____ about a population from information contained in a sample.

1.2 The Job of a Statistician

population; sample

We have noted that the objective of statistics is to make inferences about a _____ based on information contained in a _____.

Sampling implies the acquisition of data, so statistics is concerned with a theory of information. The job of a statistician is to make inferences about a population in the form of decisions or predictions, using only the information contained in a sample from that population. Using sample data to make inferences about a population introduces some uncertainty into the inference-making procedure. The job of a statistician is threefold and involves three tasks.

The first important task facing the statistician involves collection of the sample data. The sample contains a quantity of information upon which the inference about the population will be based. In fact, information can be quantified as easily as weight, heat, profit, or other quantities of interest. Consequently, it is important to decide upon the most economical procedure for buying a specified

sampling
design

quantity of information. This is called the _____ procedure or the _____ of the experiment. The cost of the specified amount of information will vary greatly depending upon the method used for collecting the data in a sample.

The second task facing a statistician involves the use of the information in a

inference

sample to make an _____ about the population from which the sample was drawn. It is his job to select an appropriate method of inference for the situation at hand. Some inferences, say, estimates of the characteristics of the population, are very accurate and consequently are good. Others are far from reality and bad. It is therefore necessary to clearly define a measure of goodness for an inference maker. Most people observe the world about them and make inferences daily. Some of these subjective inference makers are very good and accurate; others are very poor. Statistical inference makers are objective rather than subjective, but they vary in their goodness. The statistician wishes to obtain the best inference maker for a given situation.

A measure of the goodness or reliability of an inference is the third task of a statistician and is always necessary in order to assess its practical value. Thus, inference making is regarded as a two-step procedure. First, we select the best method and use it to make an _____. Second, we always give a measure of the goodness or _____ of the inference.

inference
reliability

Chapter   2

HOW TO PHRASE AN INFERENCE: GRAPHICAL METHODS

2.1 Introduction

In chapter 1, we considered the steps involved in achieving the objective of statistics, which is making _____ about a _____ from information contained in a _____. An obvious but often ignored requirement is that the sample be drawn from the population of interest to the experimenter.

inferences; population sample

   How are inferences made? First, we must be able to condense and describe data in a straightforward pictorial or graphical form. Second, we must be able to re-construct this visual representation using numerical descriptive measures that describe the salient characteristics of the visual representation. For example, where is the middle of the distribution? Are the measurements tightly grouped or widely scattered? Whether the set of data under consideration comprises an entire population or is merely a sample from a population, we must be able to agree upon numerical measures that describe the data. Inferences about a popula-tion can then be made in terms of the population by using the relevant informa-tion contained in the sample.

   This chapter will deal with four graphical methods of describing data:

   1. circle charts   3. frequency histograms
   2. bar charts   4. frequency polygons

2.2 Circle Charts

A *circle chart* or *pie chart* is a method of graphical description in which a sub-divided circle is used to represent the way in which a group of objects are distributed among a set of categories. The circle is subdivided into sectors, with each sector representing the percentage of the total contributed by a particular category.

Example 2.1

The following data represent the job classifications of 25 female university employees.

Job Classification	Frequency
1. Secretary	8
2. Administrative Staff	4
3. Instructor	6
4. Assistant Professor	4
5. Associate Professor	2
6. Full Professor	1

Construct a circle chart to depict these data.

Solution

The percentages of the total falling in each of the six categories are obtained by dividing each frequency by 25 and then multiplying by 100. For example, since 8 of the women are secretaries, the proper percentage is $(^8/_{25})(100) = ($ _____ $)$ $(100) = $ _____ $\%$. Similarly, for category 2, the percentage of the total is $(^4/_{25})(100) = ($ _____ $)(100) = $ _____ $\%$. Calculate the necessary percentages in the table below.

.32
32
.16; 16

Classification	Frequency	Percentage
1. Secretary	8	32%
2. Administrative Staff	4	16%
3. Instructor	6	_____
4. Assistant Professor	4	16%
5. Associate Professor	2	8%
6. Full Professor	1	4%

24%

The total number of degrees in a circle is _____ and the number of degrees that will be apportioned to each category is computed as a percentage of $360°$. For example, since secretaries comprise 32% of the total female workforce, this category will be represented by a sector with a central angle of

360

$$(.32)(\text{_____}) = \text{_____ degrees}$$

360; 115.2

The sector angles corresponding to the other five categories are found in the following table.

Classification	Frequency	Percentage	Sector Angle	
1. Secretary	8	32	115.2	
2. Administrative Staff	4	16	57.6	
3. Instructor	6	24	_____	86.4
4. Assistant Professor	4	16	_____	57.6
5. Associate Professor	2	8	28.8	
6. Full Professor	1	4	_____	14.4
		_____	_____	100; 360.0

The circle chart is now constructed by marking off the first five sector angles with a protractor. The remaining sector is allotted to the final category.

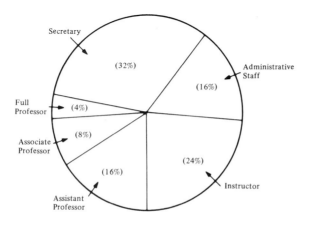

2.3 Bar Charts

In many instances, experimental data is such that the observations fall naturally into several different categories. The experimenter may define these several categories, which are _____ and _____, and then classify each observation as belonging to one of these categories or classes.

nonoverlapping;
all-inclusive

Example 2.2
a. If we wish to categorize people with respect to political affiliation, we might use the categories: Republican, Democrat, Socialist, Independent, Other.
b. We could classify people according to whether they lived in an urban, suburban, or rural area.
c. Individuals could be classified as belonging to a high, medium, or low physical-activity group.
d. Cars could be classified according to manufacturer, or according to the year in which they were made.

The *bar chart* is a method of graphical description in which the horizontal axis of a graph is used to locate the categories of interest. Rectangles are then constructed over each category, with a height corresponding to the number of observations in the category. This number is called the *frequency* or *group frequency* for the particular category of interest.

Example 2.3

The following data represent the total sales and the domestic sales for a particular company over the years 1974–1978.

	Sales (thousands of dollars)				
	1974	*1975*	*1976*	*1977*	*1978*
Domestic	250	300	350	390	400
Total	300	350	500	520	600

Construct a bar chart to depict these data.

Solution

1. The horizontal axis of the graph is used to locate the _____ of interest to the experimenter.

2. In order to incorporate domestic and total sales into one graph, the height of the bar for a particular year is taken to be the _____ sales for this year. The bar is then subdivided, with a shaded area equal to the _____ of that year's sales that were domestic.

3. The bar chart can now be constructed on the axes given below.

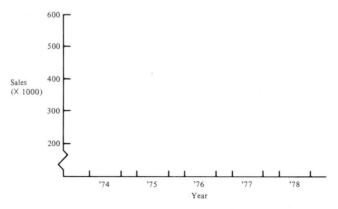

4. Using the bar chart, complete the following statements about the company's sales.

   a. Since the total sales for 1978 were $600,000 as compared to 1975 sales of $350,000, the 1978 bar is _____ times as high as the 1975 bar.

   b. Since domestic sales for 1977 were $390,000 while total sales were $520,000, the proportion of the 1977 bar that is shaded (indicating domestic sales) is _____ %.

The charts produced by graphical descriptive techniques must be interpreted with care, or the wrong conclusions may result. It is especially easy to mislead a careless reader by breaking, shrinking, or stretching the _____

Margin notes:

years

total
proportion

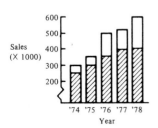

1.71

75

axes

of a graph. To protect oneself, always examine the _____ of measure-   scales
ment on graphs and charts carefully.

Self-Correcting Exercises 2A

1. The following data supplied by the Bureau of Labor Statistics gives the total
civilian labor force and those employed during the years 1970-1977.

	Civilian Labor Force ($\times 10^6$)							
	1970	1971	1972	1973	1974	1975	1976	1977
Employed	78.6	79.1	81.7	84.4	85.9	84.8	87.5	90.5
Total Labor Force	82.8	84.1	86.5	88.7	91.0	92.6	94.8	97.4

   a. Construct a bar chart to depict these data.
   b. Suppose that, for political reasons, you wanted to make the drop in
      employment due to the recession in 1975 look as large and dramatic as
      possible. Construct a bar chart that distorts the information in order to
      achieve that goal.
2. The following data are the number of persons employed during 1976 according to the following occupational groups.

Group	Millions Employed
White collar	43.7
Blue collar	29.0
Service worker	12.0
Farm worker	2.8
Total	87.5

   Construct a circle chart to depict these data.
3. The following data, provided by the Central Intelligence Agency, are the
   projected demands for oil by non-Communist nations for the years 1977–
   1979. Figures shown are millions of barrels per day.

	1977	1978	1979
United States	18.3	19.0	19.7
West Europe	14.3	14.2	14.4
Japan	5.4	5.8	6.2
Canada	2.1	2.2	2.3
Other	10.6	11.3	11.9

   a. Construct circle charts representing the projected demands for each of the
      years 1977, 1978, and 1979.

b. Construct a bar graph comparing the projected demands for the years 1977 and 1979 simultaneously.

c. Which of the two graphical methods is more effective in describing these data?

2.4 Frequency Histograms and Frequency Polygons

A third method of graphical description for a set of measurements is called the *frequency histogram.* Consider the following example.

Example 2.4
The following data are the numbers of correct responses on a recognition test consisting of 30 items, recorded for 25 students:

25	29	23	27	25
23	22	25	22	28
28	24	17	24	30
19	17	23	21	24
15	20	26	19	23

1. First find the highest score, which is _____, and the lowest score, which is _____. These two scores indicate that the measurements have a range of 15.

2. To determine how the scores are distributed between 15 and 30, we divide this interval into subintervals of equal length. The interval from 15 to 30 could be divided into from 5 to 20 subintervals, depending upon the number of measurements available. Wishing to obtain about 7 subintervals, a suitable width is determined by dividing 30 – 15 = 15 by 7. The integer _____ would seem to provide a satisfactory subinterval width for these data.

3. Utilizing the subinterval boundary points 14.5, 16.5, 18.5, 20.5, 22.5, 24.5, 26.5, _____, and _____, we guarantee that none of the given measurements will fall on a boundary point. Thus, each measurement falls into only one of the subintervals or classes.

4. We now proceed to tally the given measurements and record the class frequencies in a table. Fill in the missing information.

Tabulation of Data for Histogram

Class i	Class Boundaries	Tally	Frequency, f_i	Relative Frequency, f_i/n
1	14.5–16.5	I	1	1/25
2	16.5–18.5	II	2	2/25
3	18.5–20.5	_____	3	3/25
4	20.5–22.5	III	3	_____
5	22.5–24.5	‖‖ II	_____	7/25
6	_____	IIII	4	4/25
7	26.5–28.5	_____	3	3/25
8	28.5–30.5	II	2	2/25

Margin answers:

30
15

2

28.5; 30.5

III
3/25
7
24.5-26.5
III

5. The number of measurements falling in the ith class is called the ith class frequency and is designated by the symbol f_i. Of the total number of measurements, the fraction falling in the ith class is called the _____ frequency in the ith class. Given n measurements, the relative frequency in the ith class is given as f_i/n. As a check on your tabulation, remember that for k classes,

   relative

   a. $\Sigma\, f_i =$ _____

   n

   b. $\Sigma\, f_i/n =$ _____

   1

6. With the data so tabulated, we can now use a frequency histogram (plotting frequency against classes) or a relative frequency histogram (plotting relative frequency against classes) to describe the data. The two histograms are identical except for scale.

   a. Study the following histogram based on our data:

   Frequency Histogram

   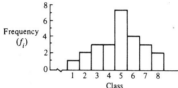

   b. Complete the following relative frequency histogram for the same data:

   Relative Frequency Histogram

   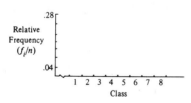

   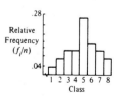

   c. When completed, the histograms in parts a and b should appear identical except for scale.

7. By examining the tabulation found in step 4, answer the following questions:

   a. What fraction of the students had scores less than 20.5? _____ .

   $^6/_{25}$ or 24%

   b. What fraction of the students had scores greater than 26.5? _____ .

   $^5/_{25}$ or 20%

   c. What fraction of the students had scores between 20.5 and 26.5?

   _____ .

   $^{14}/_{25}$ or 56%

A relative frequency distribution can also be portrayed graphically using a *frequency* or *relative frequency polygon.* Dots are placed at a height corresponding to the desired frequency or relative frequency, and at a point on the horizontal axis corresponding to the midpoint of the desired class interval. The dots are then connected to create the polygon.

Example 2.5
Using the frequency distribution given in example 2.4, the data are summarized using a relative frequency polygon. Complete the graph below.

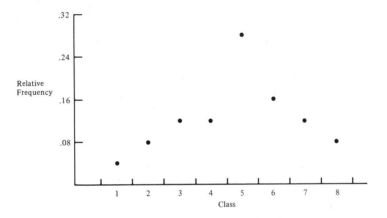

As the number of measurements in the sample increases, the sample histogram or polygon should resemble the population histogram or polygon more and more. Thus, to estimate the fraction of measurements in the entire population possessing a particular attribute, we could use the sample histogram or polygon.

A relative frequency histogram is often called a relative frequency distribution because it displays the manner in which the data are distributed along the horizontal axis of the graph. The rectangular bars above the class intervals in the relative frequency histogram can be given two interpretations:

1. The height of the bar above the ith class represents the fraction of observations falling in the ith class.
2. The height of the bar above the ith class also represents the probability that a measurement drawn at random from this sample will belong to the ith class.

Example 2.6
Refer to the data tabulation given in example 2.4 and complete the following statements.

a. An estimate of the fraction of students in the entire population having scores greater than 26.5 is _____ or _____%.

b. The probability that a measurement drawn at random from this data will fall in the interval 22.5 to 24.5 is _____.

c. The probability that a measurement drawn at random from this data will be greater than 18.5 is _____.

d. The probability that a measurement drawn at random from this data will be less than 24.5 is _____.

$^5/_{25}$; 20

$^7/_{25}$

$^{22}/_{25}$

$^{16}/_{25}$

Example 2.7
The following data represent the burning times for an experimental lot of fuses, measured to the nearest tenth of a second:

5.2	3.8	5.7	3.9	3.7
4.2	4.1	4.3	4.7	4.3
3.1	2.5	3.0	4.4	4.8
3.6	3.9	4.8	5.3	4.2
4.7	3.3	4.2	3.8	5.4

Construct a relative frequency histogram for these data.

Solution
Fill in the missing entries in the table.

Tabulation of Data

Class	Class Boundaries	Tally	Frequency	Relative Frequency
1	2.45–2.95	I	1	.04
2	2.95–3.45	III	3	_____
3	3.45–3.95	ℍℍ I	_____	.24
4	3.95–4.45	_____	7	.28
5	4.45–4.95	IIII	4	_____
6	_____	III	3	.12
7	5.45–5.95	I	1	.04

Margin notes:
.12
6
ℍℍ II
.16
4.95–5.45

Relative Frequency Histogram

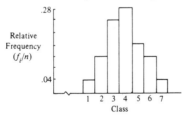

Relative Frequency (f_i/n)

Complete the following statements based on the preceding tabulation.
a. The probability that a measurement drawn at random from this sample is greater than 4.45 is _____ .
b. The probability that a measurement drawn at random from this sample is less than 3.45 is _____ .
c. An estimate of the probability that a measurement drawn at random from the sampled population would be in the interval 3.45 to 4.45 is _____ .

Margin answers:
$8/25$
$4/25$
$13/25$

Self-Correcting Exercises 2B

1. The following data are the ages in years of 42 students enrolled in an adult education class:

51	32	31	33	23	52
23	21	55	34	38	32
49	35	26	29	50	34
30	19	41	39	41	27
25	21	18	36	35	28
44	44	59	28	23	46
27	37	42	32	43	30

   a. Find the range of these data.
   b. Using about ten intervals of equal width, set up class boundaries to be used in the construction of a frequency table and complete the tabulation of the data.
   c. Construct a frequency histogram for these data.
   d. For these same data, construct a frequency histogram, utilizing about six intervals.
   e. Which histogram presents the salient points of these data more clearly?
2. The following are the annual rates of profit (in percentages) on stockholders' equity after taxes for 32 industries:

10.6	10.8	14.8	10.8
12.5	6.0	10.7	11.0
14.6	6.0	12.8	10.1
7.9	5.9	10.0	10.6
10.8	16.2	18.4	10.7
10.6	13.3	8.7	15.4
6.5	10.1	8.7	7.5
11.9	9.0	12.0	9.1

   a. Present a relative frequency histogram for these data, utilizing seven intervals of length 2, beginning at 5.55.
   b. Using the tabulation obtained in part a, construct a relative frequency polygon for the data.
   c. Using your histogram (or tabulation), answer the following questions: What is the probability that an industry drawn at random from this distribution has a rate of profit greater than 15.55%?
   d. What is the probability that an industry drawn at random has a rate of profit less than 9.55?
   e. What is the probability that an industry drawn at random has a rate of profit greater than 9.55 but less than 15.55?

EXERCISES

1. The following set of data represents the gas mileage for each of 20 cars selected randomly from a production line during the first week in March:

18.1	16.3	18.6	18.7
15.2	19.9	20.3	22.0
19.7	17.7	21.2	18.2
20.9	19.7	19.4	20.2
19.8	17.2	17.9	19.6

a. What is the range of these data?
b. Construct a relative frequency histogram for these data by using sub-intervals of width 1.0. (You might begin with 15.15.)
c. Based on the histogram in b:
   i. What is the probability that a measurement selected at random from these data will fall in the interval 17.15 to 21.15?
   ii. What is the estimated probability that a measurement taken from the population would be greater than 19.15?

2. The annual sales for a small variety store for the years 1974 through 1978 are listed below.

	1974	1975	1976	1977	1978
Cash	21,000	25,000	32,000	40,000	38,000
Credit	34,000	35,000	45,000	45,000	40,000

a. Construct a bar graph to depict the store's total sales volume for the five-year period.
b. Construct a bar graph to depict simultaneously the store's cash sales and credit sales over the five-year period.

3. The proposed 1975 federal budget dollar in terms of receipts and expenditures was presented using the following figures.

Receipts		
Individual income taxes		$ .42
Corporation income taxes		.16
Social insurance receipts		.28
From employees	$.14	
From employers	$.14	
Excise taxes		.06
Borrowing		.03
Other		.05
Total		$1.00

Expenditures	
Benefit payments to individuals	$ .37
Grants to states and localities	.17
National defense	.29
Net interest	.07
Other federal operations	.10
Total	$1.00

Depict the proposed budget using two separate pie charts.

4. The investment portfolio of pension funds of the employees of a particular company for 1965 and 1975 are listed.

Type of Asset	1965	1975
Common stocks	$600,000	$690,000
Preferred stocks	120,000	115,000
Industrial bonds	120,000	345,000
Government bonds	300,000	690,000
Real estate mortgages	60,000	460,000

Construct two separate pie charts to depict the company's portfolio composition, one to depict the composition in 1965, the other to depict the composition in 1975.

5. A company sells men's and women's clothing on the export market. Their primary export business is with Australia, Great Britain, and West Germany. Over the past five years, the dollar volume of their business with these three countries has been:

Year	Australia	Great Britain	West Germany
1974	$200,000	$250,000	$150,000
1975	210,000	240,000	130,000
1976	210,000	250,000	170,000
1977	270,000	250,000	220,000
1978	310,000	230,000	250,000

Construct a bar graph to depict simultaneously this company's sales in these three countries over the past five years.

6. Twenty-eight applicants interested in working for a government welfare program took an examination designed to measure their aptitude for social work. The following test scores were obtained:

79	97	86	76
93	87	98	68
84	88	81	91
86	87	70	94
77	92	66	85
63	68	98	88
46	72	59	79

Construct a relative frequency histogram for the test scores. (Use subintervals of width 9 beginning at 44.5.)

7. A class of 33 students was asked to rate themselves on whether they were outgoing or not. They were to rate themselves as : 1, extremely extroverted; 2, extroverted; 3, neither extroverted nor introverted; 4, introverted; 5, extremely introverted. The results are shown below.

Rating	1	2	3	4	5
Frequency	1	7	20	5	0

a. Construct a frequency histogram for the student ratings.
b. Construct a frequency polygon for the student ratings.

Chapter 3

HOW TO PHRASE AN INFERENCE: NUMERICAL METHODS

3.1 Introduction

The chief advantage to using a graphical method is its visual representation of the data. Many times, however, we are restricted to reporting our data verbally. In this case a graphical method of description cannot be used. The greatest disadvantage to a graphical method of describing data is its unsuitability for making inferences, since it is difficult to give a measure of goodness for a graphical inference. Therefore, we turn to *numerical descriptive measures.* We seek a set of numbers that characterizes the frequency distribution of the measurements and at the same time will be useful in making inferences.

We will distinguish between numerical descriptive measures for a population and those associated with a set of sample measurements. A numerical descriptive measure calculated from all the measurements in a population is called a (statistic, parameter). Those numerical descriptive measures calculated from sample measurements are called _____ .

Numerical descriptive measures are classified into two important types.
1. Measures of *central tendency* locate in some way the "center" of the data or frequency distribution.
2. Measures of *variability* measure the "spread" or dispersion of the data or frequency distribution.
Using measures of both types, the experimenter is able to create a concise numerical summary of the data.

3.2 Measures of Central Tendency

We will consider three of the more important measures of central tendency that attempt to locate the center of the frequency distribution.

parameter
statistics

The arithmetic *mean* of a set of n measurements $y_1, y_2, \ldots, y_n$ is defined to be the sum of the measurements divided by n. The symbol $\bar{y}$ is used to designate the sample mean while the Greek letter μ is used to designate the population mean.

The sample mean can be shown to have very desirable properties as an inference maker. In fact, we will use $\bar{y}$ to estimate the population mean, μ. To indicate the sum of the measurements, we will use the Greek letter Σ (sigma). Then Σy will indicate the sum of all the measurements that have been denoted by the symbol y. Using this summation notation, we can define the sample mean by formula as

$$\dfrac{\Sigma y}{n}$$

$$\bar{y} = \underline{\hspace{2cm}}$$

Example 3.1
Find the mean of the following measurements:

$$2, \ 5, \ 7, \ 10, \ 11, \ 13$$

Solution

48

$$\Sigma y = \underline{\hspace{2cm}}$$

48

$$\bar{y} = \dfrac{\Sigma y}{n} = \dfrac{\underline{\hspace{1.5cm}}}{6}$$

8

$$\bar{y} = \underline{\hspace{2cm}}$$

In addition to being an easily calculated measure of central tendency, the mean is also easily understood by all users. The calculation of the mean utilizes all the measurements and can always be carried out exactly.

One disadvantage of using the mean to measure central tendency is well known to any student who has had to pull up one low test score: the mean (is, is not) greatly affected by extreme values. For example, you might be unwilling to accept, say, an average property value of $105,000 for a given area as an acceptable measure of the middle property value if you knew that (a) the property value of a residence owned by a millionaire was included in the calculation and (b) excluding this residence, the property values ranged from $45,000 to $60,000. A more realistic measure of central tendency in this situation might be the property value such that 50% of the property values are less than this value and 50% are greater.

is

The *median* of a set of n measurements $y_1, y_2, \ldots, y_n$ is the value of y that falls in the middle when the measurements are arranged in order of magnitude. When n is even and there are two middle values, the median is taken to be the simple average of the two middle values.

Example 3.2
Find the median of the following set of measurements:

5, 3, 2, 7, 4

Solution
1. Arranging the measurements in order of magnitude, we have

2, 3, 4, 5, 7

2. The median will be the _____ ordered value. Hence the median is _____ .

third
4

Example 3.3
Find the median of the following set of measurements:

10, 8, 13, 14, 9, 8

Solution
1. Arranging the measurements in order of magnitude, we have

8, 8, 9, 10, 13, 14

2. Since $n = 6$ is even, the median will be the average of the _____ and _____ ordered values. Hence

third
fourth

$$\text{median} = \frac{\rule{2cm}{0.4pt} + \rule{2cm}{0.4pt}}{2}$$

9; 10

$$= \rule{2cm}{0.4pt}$$

9.5

Example 3.4
Find the mean and median of the following data:

5, 7, 8, 10, 10, 11, 13, 14

Solution

1. $\Sigma y = $ _____

78

78; 9.75

$$\bar{y} = \frac{\Sigma y}{n} = \frac{\rule{3cm}{0.4pt}}{8} = \rule{3cm}{0.4pt}$$

2. To find the median, we note that the measurements are already arranged in order of magnitude and that $n = 8$ is even. Therefore, the median will be the average of the fourth and fifth ordered values.

$$\text{median} = \frac{10 + 10}{2} = \rule{3cm}{0.4pt}$$

10

In the last example, the mean and median gave reasonably close numerical values as measures of central tendency. However, if the measurement $y_9 = 30$ were added to the eight measurements given, the recalculated mean would be $\bar{y} = \rule{2cm}{0.4pt}$, but the median would remain at 10, reflecting the fact that the median is a positional average unaffected by extreme values.

12

> The *mode* of a set of n measurements $y_1, y_2, y_3, \ldots, y_n$, is the value of y occurring with the greatest frequency. If there are two such values, the set is said to be *bimodal*.

Example 3.5
Find the mode of the following measurements:

$$1, \ 2, \ 3, \ 3, \ 5, \ 6, \ 8$$

Solution
The measurement that occurs with the greatest frequency is $\rule{2cm}{0.4pt}$;

3

3

therefore, the mode is $\rule{2cm}{0.4pt}$. The mode is generally not a good measure of central tendency, since data may be grouped in such a way that the greatest frequencies occur nowhere near the central area of the distribution. The mode may not even be unique because the greatest frequency can occur at more than one value. However, there are situations in which the mode might be a desirable measure. For example, a clothing manufacturer might want to know the modal dress size in a particular area of the country, so that he might market

more

(more, less) dresses of this size in the stores.

3.3 Measures of Variability

Having found measures of central tendency, we next consider measures of the variability or dispersion of the data. A measure of variability is necessary since a measure of central tendency alone does not adequately describe the data. Consider these two sets of data:

Set I. $x_1 = 9$ Set II. $y_1 = 1$

   $x_2 = 10$ $\bar{x} = \underline{\hspace{2cm}}$ $y_2 = 10$ $\bar{y} = \underline{\hspace{2cm}}$ 10; 10

   $x_3 = 11$ $y_3 = 19$

Both sets of data have a mean equal to _____ . However, the second set of   10
measurements displays much more variability about the mean than does the first
set.

   In addition to a measure of central tendency, a measure of variability is indis-
pensable as a descriptive measure for a set of data. A manufacturer of machine
parts would want very (little, much) variability in her product in order to con-   little
trol oversized or undersized parts, while an educational testing service would
be satisfied only if the test scores showed a (large, small) amount of variability   large
in order to discriminate among people taking the examination.
   We have already used the simplest measure of variability, the range.

   The *range* of a set of measurements is the difference between the
   largest and smallest measurements.

Example 3.6
Find the range for each of the following sets of data:

   Set I.   23   73   34   74
            28   29   26   17
            88   8   52   49
            37   96   32   45
            81   62   23   62

   Range = 96 – _____ = _____   8; 88

   Set II. 8.8   6.7   7.1   2.9
            9.0   0.2   1.2   8.6
            6.3   6.4   2.1   8.8

   Range = 9.0 – _____ = _____   0.2; 8.8

By examining the following distributions, it is apparent that although the range
is a simply calculated measure of variation, it alone is not adequate. Both distributions have the same range, but display different variability.

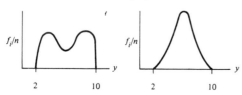

In looking for a more sensitive measure of variability, we can extend the concept
of the median as follows:

Let $y_1, y_2, \ldots, y_n$ be a set of n measurements arranged in order of increasing magnitude. The pth *percentile* is that value of y such that $p\%$ of the measurements are less than y and $(100 - p)\%$ are greater than y.

The 25th percentile is called the *lower quartile*, while the 75th percentile is called the *upper quartile*. Percentiles are more sensitive than the range in measuring variability but have the disadvantage that several percentiles must be calculated to provide an adequate description of the data.

We base the next important measure of variability on the dispersion of the data about its mean. Consider a sample of n measurements, $y_1, y_2, y_3, \ldots, y_n$. Define the sample mean as

$$\bar{y} = \underline{\hspace{2cm}}$$

$\dfrac{\Sigma y}{n}$

The quantity $(y - \bar{y})$ represents the distance (or *deviation*) of a particular measurement from the sample mean. For example, the deviation of the first measurement from the sample mean is denoted by ($\underline{\hspace{1.5cm}}$). We can calculate one deviation for each of the n measurements, for a total of $\underline{\hspace{2cm}}$ deviations. Large deviations indicate (more, less) variability of the data than do small deviations. We could utilize these deviations in different ways.

$y_1 - \bar{y}$

n

more

1. If we attempt to use the average of the n deviations, we find that the sum of the deviations is $\underline{\hspace{2cm}}$ (barring arithmetic errors). To avoid a zero sum, we could use the average of the absolute values of the deviations. This measure is difficult to calculate and is not very useful in inference making.

zero

2. More efficient use of the data is achieved by utilizing the sum of squares of these deviations. This measure, called the *sample variance*, is given by

$$s^2 = \frac{\Sigma(y - \bar{y})^2}{n - 1}$$

large; small

Large values of s^2 indicate (large, small) variability, while (large, small) values indicate small variability. To differentiate between the sample and the population variances, we use σ^2 to represent the population variance.

Since s^2 is not in the original units of measurements, we can return to these units by defining the standard deviation.

The *standard deviation, s,* is the positive square root of the variance. That is,

$$s = \sqrt{s^2} = \sqrt{\frac{\Sigma(y - \bar{y})^2}{n - 1}}$$

In the same vein, the population standard deviation is given as

$$\sigma = \sqrt{\sigma^2}$$

Example 3.7
Calculate the sample mean, variance, and standard deviation for the following data:

$$4, \ 2, \ 3, \ 5, \ 6$$

Solution
Arrange the measurements in the following way, first finding the mean, $\bar{y} =$ _____ .

4

y	$y - \bar{y}$	$(y - \bar{y})^2$
4	0	0
2	-2	4
3	-1	1
5	1	1
6	2	4

$\Sigma y = 20$ $\qquad$ $\Sigma(y - \bar{y}) =$ _____ $\qquad$ $\Sigma(y - \bar{y})^2 =$ _____

0; 10

After finding the mean, complete the second column and note that its sum is zero. The variance is

$$s^2 = \frac{\Sigma(y - \bar{y})^2}{n - 1} = \frac{}{4} = \underline{}$$

10; 2.5

while the standard deviation is

$$s = \sqrt{2.5} = \underline{}$$

1.581

Note: We will introduce a shortcut formula for calculating

$$\Sigma(y - \bar{y})^2$$

more examples will be given then.

Self-Correcting Exercises 3A

1. Fifteen brands of breakfast cereal were judged by nutritionists according to four criteria: taste, texture, nutritional value, and popularity with the buying public. Each brand was rated on a 0–5 scale for each criterion and the sum of the four ratings reported. (A high score with respect to the maximum of 20 points indicates a good evaluation of the brand.)

9	8	16	17	10
15	12	6	12	13
10	13	19	11	9

Find the mean and the median scores for these data. Compare their values.
2. The number of daily arrivals of cargo vessels at a West Coast port during an eleven-day period are given below:

3	2	0
5	4	4
2	3	2
7	1	

a. Compare the mean and median for these data.
b. Calculate the range of the data.
c. Calculate the standard deviation of the number of arrivals per day during this eleven-day period. (As an intermediate check on calculations, remember that the sum of deviations must be zero.)

3.4 On the Practical Significance of the Standard Deviation

Having defined the mean and standard deviation, we now introduce a theorem that will use both these quantities in more fully describing a set of data. This theorem can be used only if the distribution of measurements is known to be of a particular form.

> *Empirical Rule:* Given a distribution of measurements that is approximately bell-shaped, the interval
> a. $\mu \pm \sigma$ contains approximately 68% of the measurements.
> b. $\mu \pm 2\sigma$ contains approximately 95% of the measurements.
> c. $\mu \pm 3\sigma$ contains all or nearly all of the measurements.

This rule holds reasonably well for any set of measurements that possesses a distribution that is mound shaped. "Bell shaped" or "mound shaped" is taken to mean that the distribution has the properties associated with the normal distribution, whose graph is given in your text and elsewhere in this study guide.

Example 3.8
The mean and variance of a large set of measurements are 35 and 25, respectively. If this data has an approximately mound shaped distribution, describe these measurements using the Empirical Rule.

Solution
Collecting pertinent information we have

$$\bar{y} = 35, \quad s^2 = 25, \quad s = \sqrt{25} = 5$$

1. Approximately 68% of the measurements lie in the interval $35 \pm 2(5)$ or from _____ to _____ .

          25; 45

2. Approximately 95% of the measurements lie in the interval $35 \pm 3(5)$ or from _____ to _____ .

          20; 50

3. Nearly all of the measurements lie in the interval $35 \pm 4(5)$ or from _____ to _____ .

          15; 55

Example 3.9

A random sample of 100 oranges was taken from a grove and individual weights measured. The mean and variance of these measurements were 7.8 ounces and $0.36(\text{ounces})^2$, respectively. Assuming the measurements produced a mound-shaped distribution, describe these measurements using the Empirical Rule.

Solution

First find the intervals needed.

k	$\bar{y} \pm ks$	$\bar{y} - ks$	to	$\bar{y} + ks$	
1	$\bar{y} \pm s$	_____	to	_____	7.2; 8.4
2	$\bar{y} \pm 2s$	_____	to	_____	6.6; 9.0
3	$\bar{y} \pm 3s$	_____	to	_____	6.0; 9.6

Then approximately

a. _____ % of the measurements lie in the interval from _____ to _____ ,

    68; 7.2
    8.4

b. _____ % of the measurements lie in the interval from _____ to _____ ,

    95; 6.6
    9.0

c. _____ of the measurements lie in the interval from _____ to _____ .

    Nearly all; 6.0
    9.6

When n is small, the distribution of measurements (would, would not) be mound shaped and as such the Empirical Rule (would, would not) be appropriate in describing these data.

    would not
    would not

3.5   A Short Method for Calculating the Variance and Standard Deviation

The calculation of $s^2 = \Sigma(y - \bar{y})^2/(n - 1)$ requires the calculation of the quantity $\Sigma(y - \bar{y})^2$. To facilitate this calculation, we introduce the identity

$$\Sigma(y - \bar{y})^2 = \Sigma y^2 - \frac{(\Sigma y)^2}{n}$$

as a shortcut formula. This computation requires the following:

1. The ordinary arithmetic sum of the measurements, Σy
2. The sum of the squares of the measurements, Σy^2

Note the distinction between Σy^2 and $(\Sigma y)^2$ used in the identity given above.

1. To calculate Σy^2, we *first square* each measurement and *then sum* these squares.
2. To calculate $(\Sigma y)^2$, we *first sum* the measurements and *then square* this sum.

Example 3.10

Calculate s^2 and s for the data of example 3.7.

Solution

Display the data in the following way, finding Σy and Σy^2:

y	y^2
4	16
2	4
3	9
5	25
6	36
$\Sigma y = $ _____	$\Sigma y^2 = $ _____

20; 90

1. We first calculate

$$\Sigma(y - \bar{y})^2 = \frac{\Sigma y^2 - (\Sigma y)^2}{n}$$

$$= 90 - \frac{(20)^2}{5}$$

80

$$= 90 - \underline{\hspace{2cm}}$$

10

$$= \underline{\hspace{2cm}}$$

2. Then

10; 2.5

$$s^2 = \frac{\Sigma(y - \bar{y})^2}{n - 1} = \frac{\underline{\hspace{1.5cm}}}{5 - 1} = \underline{\hspace{1.5cm}}$$

1.581

$$s = \sqrt{2.5} = \underline{\hspace{2cm}}$$

Example 3.11

Calculate the mean and variance of the following data: 5, 6, 7, 5, 2, 3.

Solution

Display the data in a table.

y	y^2
5	25
6	36
7	49
5	25
2	4
3	9
$\Sigma y = \rule{2cm}{0.4pt}$	$\Sigma y^2 = \rule{2cm}{0.4pt}$

28; 148

$$\bar{y} = \frac{\Sigma y}{n} = \frac{28}{6} = \rule{2cm}{0.4pt}$$

4.67

$$\Sigma(y - \bar{y})^2 = \Sigma y^2 - \frac{(\Sigma y)^2}{n}$$

$$= 148 - \frac{(28)^2}{6}$$

$$= 148 - 130.67$$

$$= \rule{2cm}{0.4pt}$$

17.33

$$s^2 = \frac{\Sigma(y - \bar{y})^2}{n - 1} = \frac{\rule{1.5cm}{0.4pt}}{6 - 1} = \rule{1.5cm}{0.4pt}$$

17.33; 3.467

$$s = \sqrt{3.467} = 1.862$$

Self-Correcting Exercises 3B

1. Using the data given in exercise 2, Self-Correcting Exercises 3A, calculate the variance utilizing the shortcut formula to calculate the required sum of the squared deviations. Verify that the values of the variance (and hence the standard deviation) found using both calculational forms are identical.
2. If a person were concerned about accuracy due to rounding of numbers at various stages in computation, which formula for calculating $\Sigma(y - \bar{y})^2$ would be preferred:

    a. $\Sigma(y - \bar{y})^2$ or   b. $\Sigma y^2 - \frac{(\Sigma y)^2}{n}$?

Defend your choice of either a or b.
3. The following measurements represent the times required for rats to run a maze correctly: 5.2, 4.2, 3.1, 3.6, 4.7, 4.8, 4.1. Calculate the sample variance and standard deviation.
4. The heights in inches of five men consecutively entering a doctor's office were 70, 74, 69, 71, 72. Calculate the mean and variance of these heights.
5. Color identification of figures flashed on a screen is being studied. Thirty figures are flashed before each subject. It is known that the average number of colors correctly identified is 26 with a standard deviation of 1. That is, $\mu = 26$, $\sigma = 1$. It is also known that the distribution of measurements is mound shaped. Use the Empirical Rule to answer the following questions.
   a. What percentage of the subjects identify between 24 and 28 colors correctly?
   b. If one subject is chosen at random, what is the probability he will identify 25 or fewer colors correctly?

3.6 How to Guess the Standard Deviation of Sample Data

For mound-shaped or approximately normal data, we can use the range to check the calculation of s, the standard deviation. According to the Empirical Rule, approximately 95% of a set of measurements will be in the interval ($\bar{y} \pm 2s$). Hence, the sample range R should approximately equal $4s$, so that

$$s \approx \frac{R}{4}$$

This approximation requires only that the computed value be of the same order as the approximation.

Example 3.12
Check the calculated value of s for the first set of data given in example 3.6.

Solution

88

For these data, the range is 96 – 8 = _____, and

22

$$s \approx \frac{88}{4} = \text{_____}$$

would not

Comparing 22 with the calculated value, 25.46, we (would, would not) have reason to doubt the accuracy of the calculated value.

In referring to the second set of data in example 3.6, which consists of 12 measurements, we find that the range is 9.0 – 0.2 = 8.8. Hence an approximation to s using $R \approx 4s$ yields

$$s \approx \frac{(8.8)}{4} = \underline{\hspace{3cm}}$$

2.2

When compared with the calculated value 3.21, this approximation is not as close as the approximation for the first set of data.

Example 3.13
Use the data given in example 2.4 to guess the value for s. Calculate s and compare to the approximate value.

Solution
The range is 30 – 15 = \underline{\hspace{2cm}} and the approximation to s is

15

$$s \approx \frac{R}{4} = \frac{\underline{\hspace{1.5cm}}}{4} = \underline{\hspace{2cm}}$$

15; 3.75

From example 2.4, calculate $\Sigma y = 579$ and $\Sigma y^2 = 13767$. Then

$$s^2 = \frac{\Sigma(y - \bar{y})^2}{n - 1} = \frac{\Sigma y^2 - [(\Sigma y)^2 / n]}{n - 1}$$

$$= \frac{13767 - [(\underline{\hspace{1.5cm}})^2 / 25]}{24}$$

579

$$= \frac{13767 - \underline{\hspace{1.5cm}}}{24}$$

13409.64

$$= \underline{\hspace{1.5cm}}$$

14.89

$$s = \sqrt{\underline{\hspace{1.5cm}}} = \underline{\hspace{1.5cm}}$$

14.89; 3.859

which is very close to the estimated value.

EXERCISES

1. Recall that in exercise 1, chapter 2, we considered the following set of data representing the gas mileage for each of 20 cars selected randomly from a production line during the first week in March:

18.1	16.3	18.6	18.7
15.2	19.9	20.3	22.0
19.7	17.7	21.2	18.2
20.9	19.7	19.4	20.2
19.8	17.2	17.9	19.6

    a. Arrange the measurements in order of magnitude, beginning with 15.2. What is the median of these data?

    b. The _____ th percentile would be any number lying between 16.3 and 17.2.

    c. The _____ th percentile would be any number lying between 19.9 and 20.2.

    d. Calculate $\bar{y}$, s^2, and s for these data. (Remember to use the shortcut method.)

    e. Do these data conform to the Empirical Rule? Support your answer by calculating the fractions of the measurements lying in the intervals ($\bar{y} \pm ks$) for $k = 1, 2, 3$.

2. A strain of "long-stemmed roses" was developed with a mean stem length of 15 inches and standard deviation 2.5 inches. Assume that stem lengths are approximately mound shaped.

    a. If one accepts as "long-stemmed roses" only those roses with a stem length greater than 12.5 inches, what percentage of the above roses would be unacceptable?

    b. What percentage of these roses would have a stem length between 12.5 and 20 inches?

       Hint: Using the symmetry of the normal distribution, $\frac{1}{2}$ of 68% of the measurements lie one standard deviation to the left *or* to the right of the mean, and $\frac{1}{2}$ of 95% of the measurements lie two standard deviations to the left *or* to the right of the mean.

3. The heights of 40 cornstalks ranged from 2.5 feet to 6.3 feet. In presenting these data in the form of a histogram, suppose you had decided to use .5 foot as the width of your class interval.

    a. How many intervals would you use?

    b. Give the class boundaries for the first and the last classes.

4. A machine designed to dispense cups of instant coffee will dispense on the average μ ounces, with standard deviation $\sigma = .7$ ounce. Assume that the amount of coffee dispensed per cup is approximately mound shaped. If 8-ounce cups are to be used, at what value should μ be set so that approximately 97.5% of the cups filled will not overflow?

5. A pharmaceutical company wishes to know whether an experimental drug being tested in its laboratories has any effect on systolic blood pressure. Fifteen subjects, randomly selected, were given the drug, and the systolic blood pressures recorded (in millimeters) were

172	148	123
140	108	152
123	129	133
130	137	128
115	161	142

    a. Approximate s using the method described in section 3.6.

b. Calculate $\bar{y}$ and s for the data.

c. Compare the approximate and actual values for s, obtained in parts a and b.

d. Would the Empirical Rule apply to these data?

6. Toss two coins 30 times, recording for each toss the number of heads observed.

   a. Construct a histogram to display the data generated by the experiment.

   b. Find $\bar{y}$ and s for your data.

   c. Do the data conform to the Empirical Rule?

7. The following data represent the social ambivalence scores for 15 people as measured by a psychological test. (The higher the score, the stronger the ambivalence.)

9	8	15	17	10
14	11	4	12	13
10	13	19	11	9

   a. Using the range, approximate the standard deviation s.

   b. Calculate $\bar{y}$, s^2, and s for these data.

   c. What fraction of the data actually lies in the interval $(\bar{y} \pm 2s)$?

8. A lumbering company interested in the lumbering rights for a certain tract of slash pine trees is told that the mean diameter of these trees is 14 inches with a standard deviation of 2.8 inches. Assume the distribution of diameters is approximately mound shaped.

   a. What fraction of the trees will have diameters between 8.4 inches and 22.4 inches?

   b. What fraction of the trees will have diameters greater than 16.8 inches?

9. If the mean duration of television commercials on a given network is 1 minute and 15 seconds with a standard deviation of 25 seconds, what fraction of these commercials would run longer than 2 minutes and 5 seconds? Assume that duration times are approximately mound shaped.

Chapter   4

PROBABILITY AND
PROBABILITY DISTRIBUTIONS

4.1 Introduction

We have already stated that our aim is to make inferences about a population based upon sample information. However, in addition to making the inference, we also need to assess how good the inference will be.

Suppose that an experimenter is interested in estimating the unknown mean of a population of observations to within two units of its actual value. If an estimate is produced based upon the sample observations, what is the chance that the estimate is no further than two units away from the true but unknown value of the mean?

If an investigator has formulated two possible hypotheses about a population and only one of these hypotheses can be true, when the sample data are collected he must decide which hypothesis to accept and which to reject. What is the chance that he will make the correct decision?

In both these situations, we have used the term "chance" in assessing the goodness of an inference. But chance is just the everyday term for the concept statisticians refer to as _____ . Therefore, some elementary results from the theory of probability are necessary in order to understand how the accuracy of an inference can be assessed.

probability

4.2 What Is Probability?

In a general sense, we have been considering the "chance" of observing the occurrence of a particular situation or event. In order to formalize the meaning of the word "chance," we must first define some basic terminology.

An *experiment* is the process by which an observation or measurement is obtained.

experiment

Whenever data is being collected, an _____ is being performed. Some examples of experiments are:
1. Recording the height of a kindergarten student.
2. Tossing a die and recording the number appearing on the upper face.
3. Examining an altimeter to determine whether or not it is defective.
4. Recording the income of a blue collar worker.

population
sample

numerically
categorical

When an experiment is run repeatedly, a _____ of observations results. A _____ would consist of any set of observations taken from this population. Note also that when an experiment is performed, the observation obtained may be _____ valued, such as height, weight, or income, or it may be _____, such as "agree," "no decision," "disagree." However, even this last categorical response could be assigned a numerical value, such as 2, 1, and 0, respectively. An experimenter will often find it useful to have all measurements recorded numerically. Assigning a numerical score for a categorical observation is referred to as coding of data and can shortcut some work if a computer analysis of the data is available.

An experiment may result in one or more outcomes called *events*.

Example 4.1
An experiment consists of tossing a die and observing the number on the upper face. The following events might be observed.

A: Observe a 1.
B: Observe a 5.
C: Observe an odd number.
D: Observe a number greater than 2.
E: Observe either a 3 or an even number.

Example 4.2
An experiment involves ranking three applicants, *X, Y,* and *Z* in order of their ability to perform in a given position. Some possible events are:

A: *X* is ranked 1st.
B: *X* is either 1st or 2nd.
C: *Y* is 1st; *Z* is 2nd; *X* is 3rd.

Note that many different events can occur when the experiment is actually performed. We will denote these events in general by capital letters. Then, for example, if we denote an event as *A,* we will write

$P(A)$

to represent "the probability of observing the event A."

In the broadest sense, the probability of the occurrence of an event A is a measure of one's belief that the event A will occur in a single repetition of an experiment. Although a precise definition of the term "probability" is still being debated philosophically, one interpretation of this definition that finds widespread acceptance is called the *relative frequency concept* of probability. Suppose that we are interested in an event A, and are able to repeat the experiment a large number of times (N times). Further suppose that in these N repetitions, we count the number of times that the event A occurs and denote this number by n_A. As N gets large, the fraction n_A/N will approach the value _____. This concept can be formalized in the following way.

$P(A)$

The probability of the occurrence of an event A is

$$P(A) \approx \frac{n_A}{N}$$

where n_A is the number of experiments resulting in event A and N is the number of times the experiment is repeated.

It is important to notice that, since $P(A)$ is a fraction or relative frequency,

$$\underline{\hspace{2cm}} \leqslant P(A) \leqslant \underline{\hspace{2cm}}$$

$0; 1$

4.3 Additivity of Probabilities

When attempting to find the probability of an event C, it is often useful and convenient to express C in terms of other events whose probabilities are known or easily calculated. In particular, consider two events A and B and a third event C, which we will define as the event that *either A or B occurs.*

Example 4.3

Consider an experiment that can result in one of seven distinct outcomes with probabilities as given in the table.

Outcome	E_1	E_2	E_3	E_4	E_5	E_6	E_7
Probability	.05	.04	.20	.15	.36	.05	.15

Define the following events:

$$A = \{E_1, E_2, E_3\}$$

$$B = \{E_4, E_5\}$$

$$C = \{E_5, E_6, E_7\}$$

List the outcomes that comprise the following events:

D: either A or B

F: either B or C

G: either A or C

Solution

1. Since A involves outcomes E_1, E_2, E_3, and B involves outcomes E_4 and E_5, the event D involves E_1, E_2, E_3, E_4, and E_5. In particular,

$$D = \{E_1, E_2, E_3, E_4, E_5\}$$

is not

Notice that in this particular case, it (is, is not) possible to observe both events A and B on the single outcome of the experiment.

2. Since B involves E_4 and E_5 while C involves E_5, E_6, and E_7,

E_4, E_5, E_6, E_7

$$F = \{ \underline{\hspace{2cm}} \}$$

is

E_5

Notice that it (is, is not) possible to observe both B and C on a single outcome of an experiment. This will occur if outcome _____ occurs.

3. Since A involves E_1, E_2, and E_3 while C involves E_5, E_6, and E_7,

$$G = \{E_1, E_2, E_3, E_5, E_6, E_7\}$$

The situation in which two events can or cannot occur at the same time in a single repetition of an experiment is formalized as follows.

Events A and B are said to be *mutually exclusive* if (when the experiment is performed a single time) the occurrence of one of the events excludes the possibility of the occurrence of the other.

If two events are mutually exclusive, then it is possible to calculate the probability that either one or the other will occur as a sum. That is:

If events A and B are mutually exclusive,

$$P (\text{either } A \text{ or } B) = P(A) + P(B)$$

This rule can be generalized to include a set of several events, as long as they are all _____ _____ .

mutually exclusive

Example 4.4
Refer to example 4.3. Calculate $P(A)$, $P(B)$, $P(C)$, $P(D)$, $P(F)$, and $P(G)$ using the additivity law.

Solution
1. The events A, B, and C are each made up of mutually exclusive ("distinct") outcomes, by definition. Hence,

$$P(A) = P(E_1) + P(E_2) + P(E_3)$$

$$= .05 + \underline{\hspace{1cm}} + \underline{\hspace{1cm}}$$

.04; .20

$$= \underline{\hspace{1cm}}$$

.29

$$P(B) = P(E_4) + P(E_5)$$

$$= .15 + \underline{\hspace{1cm}} = \underline{\hspace{1cm}}$$

.36; .51

$$P(C) = P(E_5) + P(E_6) + P(E_7)$$

$$= .36 + .05 + \underline{\hspace{1cm}} = \underline{\hspace{1cm}}$$

.15; .56

2. Events D and G each consist of two mutually exclusive events.

$$P(D) = P(\text{either } A \text{ or } B)$$

$$= P(A) + P(B)$$

$$= .29 + \underline{\hspace{1cm}} = \underline{\hspace{1cm}}$$

.51; .80

$$P(G) = P(\text{either } A \text{ or } C)$$

$$= P(A) + P(C)$$

$$= \underline{\hspace{1cm}} + .56 = \underline{\hspace{1cm}}$$

.29; .85

3. Event F consists of two events which (are, are not) mutually exclusive. However, from part 2, example 4.3, we know that

are not

$$F = \{E_4, E_5, E_6, E_7\}$$

and that all of the E_i's are mutually exclusive. Hence,

$$P(F) = P(E_4) + P(E_5) + P(E_6) + P(E_7)$$

.36; .15; .71

$$= .15 + \underline{\hspace{1.5cm}} + .05 + \underline{\hspace{1.5cm}} = \underline{\hspace{1.5cm}}$$

Events may be related to other events in several ways. Relations between events can often be used to simplify calculations involved when finding the probability of an event. A third definition is that of an event and its *complement*.

> The *complement* of an event A is the event that A does not occur. The complement of A is denoted by the symbol $\bar{A}$.

It is always true that $P(A) + P(\bar{A}) = 1$. Therefore, $P(A) = 1 - P(\bar{A})$. If $P(\bar{A})$ can be found more easily than $P(A)$, this relationship greatly simplifies finding $P(A)$.

Example 4.5
If three fair coins are tossed, what is the probability of observing at least one head in the toss?

Solution
1. Let A be the event that there is at least one head in the toss of three coins. $\bar{A}$

no

is the event that there are \underline{\hspace{2cm}} heads in the toss of three coins.
2. There are eight possible outcomes for this experiment:

(TTT)	(TTH)
(HHT)	(THT)

HTH

(_____)	(HTT)

HHH

| (THH) | (_____) |

Intuitively, if heads and tails are equally likely, each of these outcomes should

$\frac{1}{8}$

be equally likely and would be assigned a probability of \underline{\hspace{1.5cm}}.

$\frac{1}{8}$

3. $\bar{A}$ consists of the single outcome (TTT); $P(\bar{A}) = \underline{\hspace{1.5cm}}$ and $P(A) = 1 -$

$\frac{7}{8}$

$P(\bar{A}) = \underline{\hspace{1.5cm}}$.

4.4 Conditional Probability and Independence

To introduce the concept of independence of two events, it is first necessary to define a conditional probability.

> The conditional probability of A given B, denoted as $P(A|B)$, is the probability that the event A will occur given the knowledge that the event B has already occurred.

The probability of the occurrence of event A, without any knowledge as to the occurrence or nonoccurrence of B is called the *unconditional probability* of A, or $P(A)$.

Example 4.6

Corporate executives in the Los Angeles area were interviewed and classified according to the size of the corporation they represented and their choice as to the most effective method for reducing air pollution in the Los Angeles basin. The proportions falling in each category are shown below. (Data are ficticious.)

| | Corporation Size | | |
Option	Small (A)	Medium (B)	Large (C)
Car pooling (D)	0.10	0.075	0.10
Bus expansion (E)	0.15	0.125	0.055
Gas rationing (F)	0.015	0.04	0.02
Conversion to natural gas (G)	0.05	0.035	0.025
Antipollution devices (H)	0.06	0.10	0.05

Suppose that one executive is chosen at random to be interviewed on a television broadcast. Find $P(A)$, $P(A|F)$, and $P(A|D)$.

Solution

1. The event A will occur if either of 5 mutually exclusive events occur, either A and D, A and E, _____, _____, or A and H. Hence,   *A and F; A and G*

$$P(A) = .10 + .15 + .015 + \text{_____} + \text{_____} = \text{_____}$$ *.05; .06; .375*

2. Suppose it is known that event F has occurred. That is, the executive who has been chosen is in favor of gas rationing. The group from which we are now choosing is limited to 7.5% of the total population. Moreover, it is known that this particular 7.5% is broken down by corporation size as follows:

Small (A)	Medium (B)	Large (C)
1.5%	4%	2%

Hence,

$$P(A|F) = \frac{1.5\%}{7.5\%} = .20$$

3. It is given that the chosen executive favors car pooling. Hence, we are limited to _____ of the total population. This group of executives is broken down by corporation size as follows: *27.5%*

Small (A)	Medium (B)	Large (C)
10%	7.5%	10%

Hence,

10%; .364

$$P(A|D) = \frac{\rule{2cm}{0.4pt}}{27.5\%} = \underline{\hspace{2cm}}$$

When $P(A|B) = P(A)$, the events A and B are said to be (probabilistically) independent, since the probability of the occurrence of A is not affected by knowledge of the occurrence of B. If $P(A|B) \neq P(A)$, the events A and B are said to be dependent.

Example 4.7
You hold ticket numbers 7 and 8 in an office lottery in which ten tickets numbered 1 through 10 were sold. The winning ticket is drawn at random from those sold. You are told that the winning number is odd. Does this information alter the probability that you have won the lottery or are the two events independent?

Solution
Define the events A and B as follows:

> A: Number 7 or 8 is drawn.
> B: An odd number is drawn.

$\frac{1}{5}$
$\frac{1}{5}$
independent

The unconditional probability of winning is $P(A) = \frac{2}{10} = \underline{\hspace{2cm}}$, while the conditional probability of winning is $P(A|B) = \underline{\hspace{2cm}}$. Your probability of winning remains unchanged; the events A and B are (dependent, independent).

Example 4.8
dependent
dependent

Refer to example 4.6. Since $P(A) = .375$ while $P(A|F) = .20$, events A and F are (independent, dependent). Since $P(A|D) = .364$, events A and D are (independent, dependent).

4.5 Random Variables

Most experiments result in numerical outcomes or events. The outcome itself may be a numerical quantity such as height, weight, or time, or some rank ordering of a response. When categorical observations are made—such as good or defective, color of eyes, income bracket, and so on—we are usually concerned with the number of observations falling into a specified category. Each time we observe the outcome of an experiment and assign a numerical value to the event that occurs, we are observing one particular value of a variable of interest. Since the value of this variable is determined by the outcome of a random experiment, we call the variable a *random variable.*
 Random variables are divided into two classes according to the values that the

random variable can assume. If a random variable y can take on only a finite or a countable infinity of distinct values, it is classified as a *discrete random variable*. If a random variable y can take on all the values associated with the points on a line interval, then y is called a *continuous random variable*. It is necessary to make the preceding distinction between the discrete and continuous cases because the probability distributions require different mathematical treatment. In fact, calculus is a prerequisite to any complete discussion of continuous random variables. Arithmetic and elementary algebra are all we need to develop discrete probability distributions.

The following would be examples of discrete random variables:

a. The number of voters favoring a political candidate in a given precinct
b. The number of defective bulbs in a package of twenty bulbs
c. The number of errors in an income tax return

Notice that discrete random variables are basically counts and the phrase "the number of" can be used to identify a discrete random variable. The following would be examples of continuous random variables:

a. The time required to complete a medical operation
b. The height of an experimental strain of corn
c. The amount of ore produced by a given mining operation

Classify the following random variables as discrete or continuous:

a. The number of psychological subjects responding to stimuli in a group of thirty. (_____)   discrete

b. The number of building permits issued in a community during a given month. (_____)   discrete

c. The number of amoebae in 1 cubic centimeter of water. (_____)   discrete

d. The juice content of six Valencia oranges. (_____)   continuous

e. The time to failure for an electronic system. (_____)   continuous

f. The amount of radioactive iodine excreted by rats in a medical experiment. (_____)   continuous

g. The number of defects in 1 square yard of carpeting. (_____)   discrete

Recall that in chapter 2, we selected a sample of n measurements from a population of interest and graphically described this set of data using a relative frequency distribution. These n measurements were in fact n observed values of a *random variable*. In the case of the *discrete* random variable, certain categories arise naturally (for example, the blocks of relative frequency might be centered over the integers 0, 1, 2, and so on). In the case of the *continuous* random variable, arbitrary classes are created in order to allow us to graph the distribution.

We now extend this descriptive technique to describe a population containing an infinite number of measurements. That is, we consider the set of values that can be taken by the random variable if the experiment is repeated an infinite number of times. The resulting "relative frequency" distribution is now called a _____ _____. The area under the histogram is adjusted so   probability distribution
that it is equal to one. Then, to find the probability that the random variable y falls in a given interval, one need only calculate the area under the histogram

corresponding to that interval. We will discuss two types of random variables in the remainder of this chapter, one discrete and one continuous.

4.6 The Binomial Probability Distribution

Many experiments in the social, biological, and physical sciences can be reduced to a series of trials resembling the toss of a coin whereby the outcome on each toss will be either a head or a tail. Consider the following analogies:

1. A student answers a multiple-choice question correctly (head) or incorrectly (tail).
2. A voter casts her ballot either for candidate A (head) or against him (tail).
3. A patient having been treated with a particular drug either improves (head) or does not improve (tail).
4. A subject either makes a correct identification (head) or an incorrect one (tail).
5. A licensed driver either has an accident (head) or does not have an accident (tail) during the period his license is valid.
6. An item from a production line is inspected and classified as either defective (head) or not defective (tail).

If any of the above situations were repeated n times and we counted the number of "heads" that occurred in the n trials, the resulting random variable would be a _____ random variable. Let us examine what characteristics these

binomial

experiments have in common. We will call a head a success (S) and a tail a failure (F). Note that a success does not necessarily denote a desirable outcome but rather identifies the event of interest.

The five defining characteristics of a binomial experiment are as follows:

1. The experiment consists of n identical trials.
2. Each trial results in one of two outcomes, success (S) or failure (F).
3. The probability of success on a single trial is equal to p and remains constant from trial to trial. The probability of failure is $q = 1 - p$.
4. The trials are independent.
5. Attention is directed to the random variable y, the total number of successes observed during the n trials.

Although very few real-life situations perfectly satisfy all five characteristics, this model can be used with fairly good results if the violations are "moderate." The next several examples will illustrate binomial experiments.

Example 4.9

A procedure (the "triangle test") often used to control the quality of name-brand food products utilizes a panel of n "tasters." Each member of the panel is presented three specimens, two of which are from batches of the product known to possess the desired taste while the other is a specimen from the latest batch. Each panelist is asked to select the specimen that is different from the other two. If the latest batch does possess the desired taste, then the probability that a given taster will be "successful" in selecting the specimen from the latest batch is _____. If there is no communication among the panelists, their responses will comprise n independent _____, with a probability of success on a given trial equal to _____.

$\frac{1}{3}$
trials
$\frac{1}{3}$

Example 4.10
Almost all auditing of accounts is done on a sampling basis. Thus an auditor might check a random sample of n items from a ledger or inventory list comprising a large number of items. If 1% of the items in the ledger are erroneous, then the number of erroneous items in the sample is essentially a _____ random variable with n trials and probability of success (finding an erroneous item) on a given trial equal to _____.

binomial

.01

Example 4.11
No treatment has been known for a certain serious disease for which the mortality rate in the United States is 70%. If a random selection is made of 100 past victims of this disease in the United States, the number y_1 of those in the sample who died of the disease is essentially a binomial random variable with $n =$ _____ and $p =$ _____. More important, if observation is made of the next 100 persons in the United States who will in the future become victims of this disease, the number y_2 of these who will die from the disease has a distribution approximately the same as that of y_1 if conditions affecting this disease remain essentially constant for the time period considered.

100; .70

Example 4.12
The continued operation (reliability) of a complex assembly often depends on the joint survival of all or nearly all of a number of similar components. Thus a radio may give at least 100 hours of continuous service if no more than 2 of its 10 transistors fail during the first 100 hours of operation. If the 10 transistors in a given radio were selected at random from a large lot of transistors, then each of these (ten) transistors would have the same probability p of failing within 100 hours, and the number of transistors in the radio that will fail within 100 hours is a _____ random variable with _____ trials and probability of success on each trial equal to _____. ("Success" is a word that denotes one of the two outcomes of a single trial and does not necessarily represent a desirable outcome.)

binomial; 10
p

   Three experiments are described below. In each case state whether or not the experiment is a binomial experiment. If the experiment is binomial, specify the number n of trials and the probability p of success on a given trial. If the experiment is not binomial, state which characteristics of a binomial experiment are not met.

1. A fair coin is tossed until a head appears. The number of tosses y is observed. If binomial, $n =$ _____ and $p =$ _____. If not binomial, list characteristic(s) (1, 2, 3, 4, and 5) violated. _____

[not binomial]
1, 5

2. The probability that an applicant scores above the 90th percentile on a qualifying examination is .10. The examiner is interested in y, the number of applicants (of the 25 taking the examination) that score above the 90th percentile. If binomial, $n =$ _____ and $p =$ _____. If not binomial, list characteristic(s) (1, 2, 3, 4, and 5) violated. _____

25; .10

3. A sample of 5 transistors will be selected at random from a box of 20 transistors of which 10 are defective. The experimenter will observe the number y of defective transistors appearing in the sample. If binomial, $n =$ _____ and $p =$ _____. If not binomial, list characteristic(s) (1, 2, 3, 4, and 5) violated. _____

[not binomial]

[not binomial]

3, 4

The Binomial Probability Distribution

The probability distribution for y, the number of successes in n trials, where p is the probability of success on a given trial, is given by the formula

$$P(y) = \frac{n!}{y!(n - y)!} p^y q^{n-y}$$

for the values $y = 0, 1, 2, \ldots, n$, with $q = 1 - p$, and $n! = n(n - 1)\ldots(3)(2)(1)$. We define $0! = 1$. To illustrate the use of the formula for the binomial distribution, consider the next example.

Example 4.13

The president of an agency specializing in public opinion surveys claims that approximately 70% of all people to whom the agency sends questionnaires respond by filling out and returning the questionnaire. Four such questionnaires are sent out. Let y be the number of questionnaires that are filled out and returned. Then y is a binomial random variable with $n =$ _____ and $p =$ _____.

4; .70

1. The probability that no questionnaires are filled out and returned is

$$P(0) = \frac{4!}{0!\, 4!} (.7)^0 (.3)^4$$

.0081

$$= (.3)^4 = \underline{\hspace{1.5cm}}$$

2. The probability that exactly three questionnaires are filled out and returned is

$$P(3) = \frac{4!}{3!\, 1!} (.7)^3 (.3)^1$$

.4116

$$= 4 (.343) (.3) = \underline{\hspace{1.5cm}}$$

3. The probability that at least three questionnaires are filled out and returned is

$$P(y \geqslant 3) = P(3) + P(4)$$

$$= P(3) + \frac{4!}{4! \, 0!} (.7)^4 (.3)^0$$

$$= .4116 + \underline{\hspace{2cm}} \qquad\qquad .2401$$

$$= \underline{\hspace{2cm}} \qquad\qquad .6517$$

Example 4.14

A marketing research survey shows that approximately 80% of the car owners surveyed indicated that their next car purchase would be either a compact or an economy car. Assume the 80% figure is correct, and five prospective buyers are interviewed.

a. Find the probability that all five indicate that their next car purchase would be either a compact or an economy car.

b. Find the probability that at most one indicates that his or her next purchase will be either a compact or an economy car.

Solution

Let y be the number of car owners who indicate that their next purchase will be a compact or an economy car. Then $n =$ _____ and $p =$ _____ and the distribution for y is given by

5; .8

$$P(y) = \frac{5!}{y!(5-y)!} (.8)^4 (.2)^{5-y} \qquad y = 0, 1, \ldots, 5$$

a. The required probability is $P(5)$, which is given by

$$P(5) = \frac{5!}{5! \, 0!} (.8)^5 (.2)^0$$

$$= (.8)^5$$

$$= \underline{\hspace{2cm}} \qquad\qquad .32768$$

b. The probability that at most one car owner indicates that his or her next purchase will be either a compact or an economy car will be

$$P(y \leqslant 1) = P(0) + P(1)$$

For $y = 0$,

$$P(0) = \frac{5!}{0!\,5!}(.8)^0(.2)^5$$

$$= (.2)^5$$

.00032

$$= \underline{\hspace{2cm}}$$

For $y = 1$,

$$P(1) = \frac{5!}{1!\,4!}(.8)^1(.2)^4$$

$$= 5\,(.8)\,(.0016)$$

.0064

$$= \underline{\hspace{2cm}}$$

Hence

$$P(y \leqslant 1) = .0064 + .00032$$

.00672

$$= \underline{\hspace{2cm}}$$

The Mean and Variance for the Binomial Random Variable

The mean and standard deviation of a probability distribution are important summary measures that are used to locate the center of the distribution and to describe the dispersion of the measurements about the mean. It can be shown that for a binomial experiment consisting of n trials with the probability of success equal to p,

1. The *mean* is given as $\mu = np$.
2. The *variance* is $\sigma^2 = npq$.
3. The *standard deviation* is $\sigma = \sqrt{npq}$.

When the number of trials n becomes large and p is not too close to zero or one, the Empirical Rule can be used with fairly accurate results. The interval $(np \pm 2\sqrt{npq})$ should contain approximately 95% of the distribution, while the interval $np \pm 3\sqrt{npq}$ should contain almost all of the distribution.

Example 4.15

Suppose it is known that 10% of the citizens of the United States are in favor of increased foreign aid. A random sample of 100 United States citizens is questioned on this issue.

a. Find the mean and standard deviation of y, the number of citizens favoring increased foreign aid.

b. Within what limits would we expect to find the number favoring increased foreign aid?

Solution

a. With $n = 100$ and $p = .1$,

$$\mu = np = 100(.1) = \underline{\hspace{2cm}}$$

10

$$\sigma^2 = npq = 100(.1)(.9) = \underline{\hspace{2cm}}$$

9

$$\sigma = \sqrt{npq} = \sqrt{\underline{\hspace{1.5cm}}} = \underline{\hspace{1.5cm}}$$

9; 3

b. From part a, $\mu = 10$ and $\sigma = 3$. Using two standard deviations we find the interval $(\mu \pm 2\sigma)$ to be $[10 \pm 2(3)]$ or (10 ± 6). Since approximately 95% of the distribution lies within this interval, we would expect the number of citizens favoring increased foreign aid to lie between _____ and _____ if, in fact, $p = .1$.

4; 16

Example 4.16

Each person in a random sample of 64 people was asked to state a preference for candidate A or candidate B. If there is no underlying preference for either candidate, then the probability that an individual chooses candidate A will be $p = \underline{\hspace{2cm}}$.

.5

a. What will be the expected number and standard deviation of preferences for candidate A?

b. Within what limits would you expect the number of stated preferences for candidate A to lie?

Solution

Let y be the number of people stating a preference for candidate A. If there really is no preference for either candidate (that is, the voter selects a candidate at random), then y has a binomial distribution with $n = 64$ and $p = \underline{\hspace{2cm}}$.

.5

a. $$\mu = np = 64(.5) = \underline{\hspace{2cm}}$$

32

$$\sigma^2 = npq = 64(.5)(.5) = \underline{\hspace{2cm}}$$

16

$$\sigma = \sqrt{npq} = \underline{\hspace{2cm}}$$

4

b. From part a, $\mu = 32$ and $\sigma = 4$. Hence, $(\mu \pm 2\sigma) = (32 \pm 8)$. We would expect the number of preferences for candidate A to lie between _____ and

24

_____ if, in fact, $p = .5$.

40

Self-Correcting Exercises 4A

1. A city planner claims that 20% of all apartment dwellers move from their apartments within a year from the time they first moved in. In a particular

city, 7 apartment dwellers who had given notice of termination to their landlords are to be interviewed.

    a. If the city planner is correct, what is the probability that 2 of the 7 had lived in the apartment for less than one year?

    b. What is the probability that at least 6 had lived in their apartment for one year or more?

2. Suppose that a subject is taught to do a task in two different ways. Studies have shown that, when subjected to mental strain and asked to perform the task, the subject most often reverts to the method first learned, regardless of whether it was more difficult or easier than the second. If the probability that a subject returns to the first method learned is .8 and 6 subjects are tested, what is the probability that at least 5 of the subjects revert to their first-learned method when asked to perform their task under mental strain?

3. Harvard University has found that about 90% of its accepted applicants for enrollment in the freshman class will actually take a place in that class. In 1967, 1360 applications to Harvard were accepted. Within what limits would you expect to find the size of the freshman class at Harvard in the fall of 1967?

4. Suppose that 20% of the registered voters in a given city belong to a minority group and that voter registration lists are used in selecting potential jurors. If 80 persons were randomly selected from the voter registration lists as potential jurors, within what limits would you expect the number of minority members on this list to lie?

5. A television network claims that its Wednesday evening prime time program attracts 40% of the television audience. If the 40% figure is correct and if each person in a random sample of 400 television viewers was asked whether he or she had seen the previous show, within what limits would you expect the number of viewers who had seen the previous show to lie? What would you conclude if the interviews revealed that 96 of the 400 had actually seen the previous show?

6. On a certain university campus, a student is fined $1.00 for the first parking violation of the academic year. The fine is doubled for each subsequent offense, so that the second violation costs $2.00, the third $4.00, and so on. The probability that a parking violation on a given day is detected is .10. Suppose that a certain student will park illegally on each of 6 days during a given academic year.

    a. What is the probability he will not be fined?

    b. What is the probability that his fines will total no more than $3.00?

4.7 The Normal Probability Distribution

discrete

continuous

discrete

Random variables can be divided into two categories, (1) _____ random variables and (2) _____ random variables. While the probability distribution or frequency distribution of a _____ random variable can be represented by a relative frequency histogram, the probability distribution for a continuous random variable is represented by a smooth curve. The probability distribution for the normal random variable y is a commonly occurring and important continuous random variable, which produces the _____-shaped curve shown below.

bell

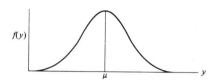

The quantity μ is a constant that represents the population _____ of the random variable y. The shape of the normal curve also depends upon a quantity denoted as σ, a constant that represents the population _____ _____ of y.

mean

standard deviation

The smooth curve representing the normal distribution can be considered to be the limiting form of a relative frequency histogram. Recall that for a relative frequency histogram with class intervals of unit length:

a.   The area of the bar over a class interval is equal to the relative frequency in that class and represents the probability that an observation falls in that class.

b.   The area under the histogram is one and represents the sum of the relative frequencies.

If the number of observations increases beyond bound while the number of intervals gets larger and larger and the width of the class interval gets smaller and smaller, the tops of the histogram bars trace a smooth curve and the width of each interval approaches zero. This brings to light some important properties of continuous distributions.

a. The area under the curve, like the area under a histogram, is adjusted to equal one.

b. Since the area of the bar over the point a equals zero, $P(y = a) = 0$.

c. $P(a < y < b)$ is given by the area under the curve between the points a and b.

We will use the properties of a continuous distribution in finding probabilities associated with a normal random variable.

The Standard Normal Probability Distribution

Probability is the vehicle through which we are able to make inferences about a population in the form of either estimation or decisions. To make inferences about a normal population, we must be able to compute or otherwise find the probabilities associated with a normal random variable. The probability that the normal random variable y lies between two points a and b is equivalent to the

μ; σ

standard

right

area

a; b

symmetric

area under the normal curve between a and b. However, since the probability distribution for a normal random variable y depends on the population parameters _____ and _____, we would be required to recalculate the probabilities associated with y each time a new value for μ or σ was encountered. We resort to a standardization process whereby we convert a normal random variable y to a _____ normal random variable z, which represents the distance of y from its mean μ in units of the standard deviation σ. To standardize a normal random variable y, we use the following procedure:

1. From y, subtract its mean μ:

$$y - \mu$$

This results in the signed distance of y from its mean, a negative sign indicating that y is to the left of μ while a positive sign indicates y is to the _____ of μ.

2. Now divide by σ:

$$\frac{y - \mu}{\sigma}$$

Dividing by σ converts the signed distance from the mean to the number of standard deviations to the right or left of μ.

3. Define

$$z = \frac{y - \mu}{\sigma}$$

z is the standard normal variable having the standardized normal distribution with mean 0 and standard deviation 1.

Given the curve representing the distribution of a continuous random variable y, the probability that $a \leq y \leq b$ is represented by the _____ under the curve between the points _____ and _____. Hence, in finding probabilities associated with a standardized normal variable z, we could refer directly to the areas under the curve. These areas are tabulated for your convenience in table 1 of the text.

Since the standardized normal distribution is _____ about the mean 0, half of the area lies to the left of 0 and half to the right of 0. Further, the areas to the left of the mean $z = 0$ can be calculated by using the corresponding and equal area to the right of $z = 0$. Hence table 1 exhibits areas only for positive values of z correct to the nearest hundredth. Table 1 gives the area between $z = 0$ and a specified value of z, say z_0. A convenient notation used to designate the area between $z = 0$ and z_0 is $A(z_0)$.

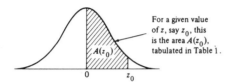

For a given value of z, say z_0, this is the area $A(z_0)$, tabulated in Table 1.

$A(z_0)$

0   z_0

a. For $z = 1$, the area between $z = 0$ and $z = 1$ is $A(z = 1) = A(1) = .3413$.

b. For $z = 2$, $A(z = 2) = A(2) = $ _____ .   .4772

c. For $z = 1.6$, $A(1.6) = $ _____ .   .4452

d. For $z = 2.4$, $A(2.4) = $ _____ .   .4918

Now try reading the table for values of z given to two decimal places.

e. For $z = 2.58$, $A(2.58) = $ _____ .   .4951

f. For $z = .75$, $A(.75) = $ _____ .   .2734

g. For $z = 1.69$, $A(1.69) = $ _____ .   .4545

h. For $z = 2.87$, $A(2.87) = $ _____ .   .4979

We will now find probabilities associated with the standard normal random variable z by using table 1.

Example 4.17

Find the probability that z is greater than 1.86, that is, $P(z > 1.86)$.

Solution

Illustrate the problem with a diagram as follows:

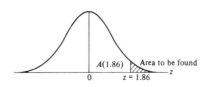

$A(1.86)$ Area to be found
z
0    $z = 1.86$

1. The total area to the right of $z = 0$ is equal to .5000.

2. From table 1, $A(1.86) = $ _____ .   .4686

3. Therefore, the shaded area is found by subtracting $A(1.86)$ from _____ .   .5000

4. Hence

$$P(z > 1.86) = .5000 - A(1.86)$$

$$= .5000 - \text{_____}$$ .4686

$$= \text{_____}$$ .0314

Example 4.18

Find $P(z < -2.22)$.

Solution

Illustrate the problem with a diagram.

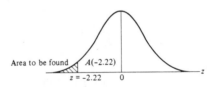

1. Using the symmetry of the normal distribution,

.4868

$$A(-2.22) = A(2.22) = \underline{\hspace{2cm}}$$

left

The negative value of z indicates that you are to the (left, right) of the mean, $z = 0$.

.4868; .0132

2. $P(z < -2.22) = .5000 - \underline{\hspace{1.5cm}} = \underline{\hspace{1.5cm}}$

Example 4.19

Find $P(-1.21 < z < 2.43)$.

Solution

Illustrate the problem with a diagram.

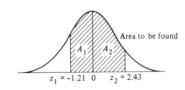

$$P(-1.21 < z < 2.43) = P(-1.21 < z < 0) + P(0 < z < 2.43)$$

.3869; .4925

$$= \underline{\hspace{2cm}} + \underline{\hspace{2cm}}$$

.8794

$$= \underline{\hspace{2cm}}$$

A second type of problem that arises is that of finding a value of z, say z_0, such that a probability statement about z will be true. We explore this type of problem with examples.

Example 4.20

Find the value of z_0 such that $P(0 < z < z_0) = .3925$.

Solution

Once again, illustrate the problem with a diagram and list the pertinent information.

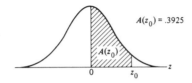

1. Search table 1 until the area .3925 is found. The value such that

$$A(z_0) = .3925 \quad \text{is} \quad z_0 = \underline{\hspace{1.5cm}}$$

1.24

2. $P(0 < z < \underline{\hspace{1.5cm}}) = .3925$

1.24

Example 4.21
Find the value of z_0 such that $P(z > z_0) = .2643$.

Solution
Illustrate the problem and list the pertinent information.

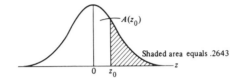

Shaded area equals .2643

1. $A(z_0) = .5000 - .2643 = \underline{\hspace{1.5cm}}$

.2357

2. The value of z_0 such that

$$A(z_0) = \underline{\hspace{1.5cm}} \quad \text{is} \quad z_0 = \underline{\hspace{1.5cm}}$$

.2357; .63

3. $P(z > \underline{\hspace{1.5cm}}) = .2643$

.63

Use of the Table for the Normal Random Variable y
We can now proceed to find probabilities associated with any normal random variable y having mean μ and standard deviation σ. This is accomplished by converting the random variable y to the standard normal random variable z, and then working the problem in terms of z.

Example 4.22
Let y be a normal random variable with mean $\mu = 100$ and standard deviation $\sigma = 4$. Find $P(92 < y < 104)$.

Solution
To calculate the desired area under the normal curve, we first determine the distance that y lies from the mean, μ, measured in standard deviations, given by

$$z = \frac{y - \mu}{\sigma}$$

1. The value $y = 92$ lies

-2

$$z = \frac{y - \mu}{\sigma} = \frac{92 - 100}{4} = \underline{\hspace{2cm}}$$

standard deviations below the mean.
2. The value $y = 104$ lies

1

$$z = \frac{y - \mu}{\sigma} = \frac{104 - 100}{4} = \underline{\hspace{2cm}}$$

standard deviation above the mean.
3. The problem can now be stated in terms of z, and is readily solved.

$$P(92 < y < 104) = P(-2 < z < 1)$$

$$= A(-2) + A(1)$$

.4772; .3413

$$= \underline{\hspace{2cm}} + \underline{\hspace{2cm}}$$

.8185

$$= \underline{\hspace{2cm}}$$

Example 4.23
Let y be a normal random variable with mean 100 and standard deviation 4. Find $P(93.5 < y < 105.2)$.

Solution

$$P(93.5 < y < 105.2) = P\left(\frac{93.5 - 100}{4} < z < \frac{105.2 - 100}{4}\right)$$

1.30

$$= P(-1.63 < z < \underline{\hspace{2cm}})$$

.4484; .4032

$$= \underline{\hspace{2cm}} + \underline{\hspace{2cm}}$$

.8516

$$= \underline{\hspace{2cm}}$$

Self-Correcting Exercises 4B

1. Find the following probabilities associated with the standard normal random variable z:

a. $P(z > 2.1)$.

d. $P(-2.75 < z < -1.70)$.

b. $P(z < -1.2)$.

e. $P(-1.96 < z < 1.96)$.

c. $P(.5 < z < 1.5)$.

f. $P(z > 1.645)$.

2. Find the value of z, say z_0, such that the following probability statements are true:

a. $P(z > z_0) = .10$.

c. $P(-z_0 < z < z_0) = .95$.

b. $P(z < z_0) = .01$.

d. $P(-z_0 < z < z_0) = .99$.

3. An auditor has reviewed the financial records of a hardware store and has found that its billing errors follow a normal distribution with mean and standard deviation equal to $0 and $1, respectively.
   a. What proportion of the store's billings are in error by more than $1?
   b. What is the probability that a billing represents an overcharge of at least $1.50?
   c. What is the probability that a customer has been undercharged from $.50 to $1.00?
   d. Within what range would 95% of the billing errors lie?
   e. Of the extreme undercharges, 5% would be at least what amount?
4. If y is normally distributed with mean 10 and variance 2.25, evaluate the following probabilities:

a. $P(y > 8.5)$.

d. $P(7.5 < y < 9.2)$.

b. $P(y < 12)$.

e. $P(12.25 < y < 13.25)$.

c. $P(9.25 < y \ 11.25)$.

5. An industrial engineer has found that the standard household light bulbs produced by a certain manufacturer have a useful life that is normally distributed with a mean of 250 hours and a variance of 2500.
   a. What is the probability that a randomly selected bulb from this production process will have a useful life in excess of 300 hours?
   b. What is the probability that a randomly selected bulb from this production process will have a useful life between 190 and 270 hours?
   c. What is the probability that a randomly selected bulb from this production process will have a useful life not exceeding 260 hours?
   d. Ninety percent of the bulbs have a useful life in excess of how many hours?
   e. The probability is .95 that a bulb does not have a useful life in excess of how many hours?

6. Scores on a trade school entrance examination exhibit the characteristics of a normal distribution with mean and standard deviation of 50 and 5, respectively.
    a. What proportion of the scores on this examination would be greater than 60?
    b. What proportion of the scores on this examination would be less than 45?
    c. What proportion of the scores on this examination would be between 35 and 65?
    d. If to be considered eligible for a place in the incoming class an applicant must score beyond the 75th percentile on this exam, what score must an applicant have to be eligible?

4.8 Summary

The objective of statistics is to make inferences about a population based upon sample information. In order to assess the accuracy or goodness of an inference, we turn to the concepts of probability and probability distributions to supply a means of error assessment.

Since most experiments result in numerically valued outcomes, sample data represent observed values of random variables. To extract the information contained in samples, we begin by studying the probability distributions of random variables. Random variables are of two types, discrete and continuous. Their probability distributions can be derived mathematically using probability models, or can be approximated by observing the results of a large number of repetitions of the experiment giving rise to that random variable.

The binomial probability distribution is the distribution of a discrete random variable y, defined as the total number of successes observed in n independent and identical trials, each of which results in either success or failure. The probability of success on a given trial is defined as p and remains constant from trial to trial. Probabilities associated with this random variable can be found by calculating individually

$$P(y) = \frac{n!}{y!(n-y)!} p^y q^{n-y}$$

for the desired values of y and summing the necessary probabilities.

The normal probability distribution is the distribution of a continuous random variable y, and occurs quite frequently in nature. Probabilities associated with this random variable can be found by using a standardizing procedure to relate all desired values of y to the number of standard deviations those values lie from their mean, μ.

EXERCISES

1. Give a random variable y with the probability distribution

y	$P(y)$
1	$\frac{1}{8}$
2	$\frac{5}{8}$
3	$\frac{1}{4}$

  a. Graph $P(y)$ and make a visual approximation to the mean.
  b. Calculate $P(y \leqslant 2); P(y \geqslant 3)$.
2. A large commercial bank has branch banks located throughout five western states. The 120 branch banks are categorized below according to the state in which they are located and the number of years they have been in operation.

	State				
	Washington	Oregon	California	Nevada	Idaho
Under 5	11	9	17	3	6
5–10	12	5	23	4	3
Over 10	7	6	10	3	1

A bank is selected at random from among the 120 branch banks.
  a. Find the probability that the bank is located in Washington.
  b. Find the probability that the bank has been in operation less than 5 years.
  c. Find the probability that the bank has been in operation at least 5 years.
  d. Find the probability that the bank is in California or has been in operation over 10 years, or both.
  e. Find the probability that the bank has been in operation at least 5 years or is located in Oregon or both.
  f. Find the probability that the bank is located in Washington and has been in operation at least 10 years.
  g. Given that the bank has been in operation less than 5 years, find the probability that it is located in Idaho.
  h. Given that the bank is located in California, find the probability that it has been in operation 10 years or less.
  i. Find the probability that the bank is located outside of California.
3. In the past history of a certain serious disease it has been found that about ½ of its victims recover.
  a. Find the probability that exactly 4 of the next 5 patients suffering from this disease will recover.
  b. Find the probability that at least 4 of the next 5 patients afflicted with this disease will recover.
4. Suppose that 70% of the first-class mail from New York to California is

delivered within 4 days after being mailed. If 10 pieces of first-class mail are mailed from New York to California:

a. Find the probability that at least 9 pieces of mail arrive within 4 days of the mailing date.

b. Find the probability that 2 or fewer pieces of mail arrive later than 4 days after the mailing date.

5. A subject participating in an identification experiment is shown an object for 0.1 second and then asked to select that object from among a group of 5 objects. The experimenter records the identification as correct or incorrect for each of five trials. If the subject's perception time is longer than 0.1 second then he would be forced to choose randomly one of the five objects for identification with p, the probability of a correct identification being $\frac{1}{5}$ = 0.2.

a. Find the probability that the subject correctly identifies none of the objects if his perception time is longer than 0.1 second.

b. Find the probability that the subject correctly identifies at least 4 of the objects.

6. To test two methods of presentation of a given subject, ten pairs of identical twins were selected and one from each pair was randomly assigned to method A, the other to method B. At the end of the teaching periods, all the twins were given the same test and their grades were recorded. Let y be the number of twins taught using method A who did better on the exam than their respective twin taught by method B.

If there is really no difference between the two methods, the probability that twin A does better than twin B on the exam can be taken to be $p = .5$. What is the probability that 8 or more twins in the A group did better than their "B twins"?

7. Find the following probabilities for the standard normal variable z:

a. $P(z < 1.9)$.

d. $P(-2.8 < z < 1.93)$.

b. $P(1.21 < z < 2.25)$.

e. $P(-1.3 < z < 2.3)$.

c. $P(z > -.6)$.

f. $P(-1.62 < z < .37)$.

8. Find the value of z, say z_0, such that the following probability statements are true:

a. $P(z > z_0) = .2420$.

c. $P(-z_0 < z < z_0) = .90$.

b. $P(-z_0 < z < z_0) = .9668$.

d. $P(z < z_0) = .9394$.

9. If y is distributed normally with mean 25 and standard deviation 4, find the following:

a. $P(y > 21)$. c. $P(15 < y < 35)$.

b. $P(y < 30)$. d. $P(y < 18)$.

10. A psychological introvert-extrovert test produced scores that had a normal distribution with mean and standard deviation 75 and 12, respectively. If we wish to designate the *highest* 15% as extrovert, what would be the proper score to choose as the cutoff point?

11. A manufacturer's process for producing steel rods can be regulated so as to produce rods with an average length μ. If these lengths are normally distributed with a standard deviation of .2 inch, what should be the setting for μ if one wants at most 5% of the steel rods to have a length greater than 10.4 inches?

12. For a given type of cannon and a fixed range setting, the distance that a shell fired from this cannon will travel is normally distributed with a mean and standard deviation of 1.5 and .1 miles, respectively.

a. What is the probability that a shell will travel farther than 1.72 miles?

b. What is the probability that a shell will travel less than 1.35 miles?

c. What is the probability that a shell will travel at least 1.45 miles but at most 1.62 miles?

Chapter 5
SAMPLING DISTRIBUTIONS

5.1 Introduction

Recall from earlier discussions that a population of measurements results when an experiment is repeated an infinite number of times. This population can be described using numerical descriptive measures called _____ . A sample is some subset of the population, and can be described using numerical descriptive measures called _____ . One of our objectives will be to use statistics (calculated from the sample) to make inferences about (or estimate) a population parameter.

   Since a statistic is computed from sample measurements, to observe the statistic over and over again, we must sample repeatedly. This repeated sampling will generate a population of possible values of the statistic. The frequency distribution associated with the population of values of the statistic is called its _____ _____ . Specifically, since it is generated through repeated sampling, this probability distribution is called a *sampling distribution*.

   In this chapter, we will discuss a common method used to obtain a sample, as well as the sampling distributions of some important sample statistics.

parameters

statistics

probability distribution

5.2 Random Sampling

The objective of the study of statistics is to allow the experimenter to make inferences about a population from information contained in a _____ . Since it is the sample that provides the information that is used in inference making, we must be duly careful about the selection of the elements in the sample so that we do not systematically exclude or include certain elements of the population in our sampling plan. The sample should be representative of the population being sampled.

sample

We call a sample that has been drawn without bias a *random sample.* This is a shortened way of saying that the sample has been drawn in a random manner. Several types of random samples are available for use in a particular situation, depending on the scope of the experiment and the objectives of the experimenter. A commonly employed and uncomplicated sampling plan is called the *simple random sample.*

> A *simple random sample* of size *n* is said to have been drawn if each possible sample of size *n* in the population has the same chance of being selected.

Example 5.1
A medical technician needs to choose two animals for testing from a cage containing four animals. How many samples are available to the technician? List these samples.

Solution
6

There are _____ ways to choose two animals from a total of four. Designating each animal by a number from 1 to 4, the samples are

1, 4
3, 4

$$(1, 2) \qquad (1, 3) \qquad (\underline{\hspace{2cm}})$$
$$(2, 3) \qquad (2, 4) \qquad (\underline{\hspace{2cm}})$$

$\frac{1}{6}$

random number

0; 9

A simple random sampling plan for this experiment would allow each of these 6 possible samples an equal chance of being selected, namely, _____.

Although random sampling is difficult to achieve in practice, the use of a _____ _____ table in selecting a random sample is the best way to implement a random sampling design. A random number table contains the digits _____ through _____ with equal frequency and in a random order. The digits are in random order if there is no pattern of any kind with respect to their occurrence. For example, in a random number table you would not find the digit 9 always followed by a 1 or 2. Neither, for example, would you find a two-digit combination such as 57 or 75 always followed by a combination such as 68 or 86. When a random number table is used to select a simple random sample, the choice of elements to be included in the sample reflects the properties of the random number table used in the selection. We illustrate the procedure with the next example.

Example 5.2
In order to estimate the number of visits to a doctor per household in an area containing $N = 1000$ households, an investigator has decided to select a simple random sample of size 20 households. Use the random number table in your text to select a sample of size $n = 20$ drawn in such a way as to satisfy a simple random sampling plan.

Solution

The set to be sampled consists of a list of the 1000 households in the given area. Since each of the numbers 1 through 1000 corresponds to one and only one household in the area, we need to select 20 numbers between 1 and 1000 from the random number table to identify the households to be included in the sample.

a. Suppose we decide to use the first three digits of the five-digit numbers appearing in the columns of the table. We must first randomly select a line and column in the table as a starting point and then decide in which direction we will move within the table. This can be done by turning to a page containing the random numbers and setting your pencil point on the page. In pinpointing a five-digit block of numbers, we can use the first two digits to find the row and the next two digits to find the column in which to begin. Suppose that our pencil pointed to the five-digit group 21932 in line 22, column 1. The first two digits in the group 21932 can identify the line as line _____, while the second two digits in the group 21932 can identify the column. Since there are only 10 columns, divide 93 by 10 and use the *remainder* to identify the column. Since 93/10 is 9 with a remainder of _____, we begin with column _____.

b. Using line 21, column 3 as a starting point, we can now list the five-digit entries by moving in any direction we wish. Let us list lines 21 through 25 for columns 3, 4, 5, and 6 to produce the 20 random numbers required to identify the sample elements. We will associate households 1 through 999 with the entries 001 through 999 in the table and household 1000 with the entry 000.

01205	08978	43021	77321
75464	43497	81807	99369
78638	75114	42943	81629
14952	55565	98821	92843
92770	11506	34101	01051

By reading the first three digits in each five-digit group, we have identified the households to be included in the sample.

c. If a household number appeared more than once in the list of random numbers, that household would only appear *once* in the sample. Further entries in the table would be used until 20 distinct households had been identified for inclusion in the sample.

Example 5.3

How would the selection procedure in example 5.2 be modified if the area contained $N = 500$ households?

Solution

a. By using three-digit entries to identify the $n = 20$ households when the popu-

21

3; 3

001; 500

500

728
500

lation size is $N = 500$, we could associate households 1 through 500 with the digits _____ through _____ and discard or not record 000 and any random digits between 501 and 999.

b. Alternatively, to avoid excessive table listings, we could use the random digits 001 through 500 directly, and for any number in the range 501 through 999, use its remainder upon division by _____ . Under this scheme, household 228 would be associated with the three-digit random numbers 228 and _____ . Finally, by associating household 500 with the random numbers 000 and _____ , our sample will be drawn so that every household has a 2 in 1000 or 1 in 500 chance of being included in the sample.

Self-Correcting Exercises 5A

1. An auditing firm has been hired by a company to examine the company's accounts receivable. If the company has 100 current accounts and the auditing firm proposes to examine 20 of those accounts, explain how you would randomly select 20 accounts from the 100 accounts using a random number table.

2. To investigate employee satisfaction with regard to company fringe benefits, the management of a company employing 250 workers proposes to survey 30 workers concerning their views on company fringe benefits. If these 30 workers are to be randomly chosen from the 250 workers employed by the company, provide an efficient selection scheme for choosing the 30 workers, using the random number tables. Implement the sampling plan and record the 30 workers who are to be interviewed.

5.3 The Central Limit Theorem and the Sampling Distribution of a Sample Mean

Consider an experiment whereby the distance traveled by a shell fired from a given cannon is measured and recorded. If none of the settings on the cannon were changed and this experiment were repeated a large number of times, a frequency histogram of these distances would probably exhibit the mound-shaped distribution characteristic of the normally distributed random variable. Why should this be the case? The cannon undoubtedly has some sort of average firing distance, but each measurement would deviate from this value due perhaps to errors in measurement by the person recording the distance, the air temperature or humidity at the time of firing, the exact amount of gun powder in the chamber, the angle of the cannon when fired, and so on. Hence any one distance would consist of an average distance modified by the addition of random errors, which might be either positive or negative.

The Central Limit Theorem loosely stated says that sums or averages are approximately normally distributed with a mean and standard deviation that depend on the sampled population. By thinking of the error in the distance measured (the deviation from the "average distance") as a *sum* of various effects in which small errors are highly likely and large errors are highly improbable, the Central Limit Theorem helps explain the apparent normality of the shell distances.

Further, and just as important, the Central Limit Theorem assures us that sample means will be approximately normally distributed with a mean and variance that depend on the population from which the sample has been drawn. This aspect of the Central Limit Theorem will be the focal point for making inferences about populations based on random samples when the sample size is large.

> *The Central Limit Theorem (1):* If random samples of n observations are drawn from a population with finite mean μ and standard deviation σ, then when n is large, the sample mean $\bar{y}$ will be approximately normally distributed with mean μ and standard deviation $\sigma/\sqrt{n}$.

The Central Limit Theorem could also be stated in terms of the sum of the measurements, Σy.

> *The Central Limit Theorem (2):* If random samples of n observations are drawn from a population with finite mean μ and standard deviation σ, then when n is large, Σy will be approximately normally distributed with mean $n\mu$ and standard deviation $\sigma\sqrt{n}$.

In both cases the approximation to normality becomes more and more accurate as n becomes large.

The Central Limit Theorem is important for two reasons.

1. It partially explains *why* certain measurements possess approximately a
   _____ distribution.   normal

2. Many of the _____ used in making inferences are sums or means of   estimators
   sample measurements and thus possess approximately _____ dis-   normal
   tributions for large samples. Notice that the Central Limit Theorem (does,   does not
   does not) specify that the sample measurements come from a normal population. The population (could, could not) have a frequency distribution that is   could
   flat or skewed or is nonnormal in some other way. It is the *sample mean* that
   behaves as a random variable having an approximately normal distribution.

To clarify a point we note that the sample mean $\bar{y}$ computed from a random sample of n observations drawn from any population with mean μ and a standard deviation σ always has a mean equal to μ and a standard deviation equal to $\sigma/\sqrt{n}$. This result is not due to the Central Limit Theorem. The important contribution of the theorem lies in the fact that when n, the sample size, is *large*, we may approximate the distribution of $\bar{y}$ with a *normal* probability distribution.

Example 5.4

A production line produces items whose mean weight is 50 grams with a standard deviation of 2 grams. If 25 items are randomly selected from this production line, what is the probability that the sample mean $\bar{y}$ exceeds 51 grams?

Solution

According to the Central Limit Theorem, the sample mean $\bar{y}$ is approximately normally distributed with mean μ and standard deviation $\sigma/\sqrt{n}$. For our problem $\mu = 50$, $\sigma = 2$, and $n = 25$; hence

.4

$$\sigma_{\bar{y}} = \frac{\sigma}{\sqrt{n}} = \frac{2}{\sqrt{25}} = \underline{\hspace{2cm}}$$

Therefore

$$P(\bar{y} > 51) = P\left(\frac{\bar{y} - 50}{.4} > \frac{51 - 50}{.4}\right)$$

$$= P(z > 2.5)$$

$$= .5000 - A(2.5)$$

.4938

$$= .5000 - \underline{\hspace{1.5cm}}$$

.0062

$$= \underline{\hspace{1.5cm}}$$

Example 5.5

A bottler of soft drinks packages cans of soft drink in six-packs.
a. If the fill per can has a mean of 12 fluid ounces and a standard deviation of .2 fluid ounce, what is the distribution of the total fill for a six-pack?
b. What is the probability that the total fill for a six-pack is less than 71 fluid ounces?

Solution

a. Using the Central Limit Theorem in its second form, the total fill per six-pack
72   has a mean of $n\mu = 6(12) = \underline{\hspace{1.5cm}}$ fluid ounces and a standard deviation
.49   of $\sigma\sqrt{n} = .2\sqrt{6} = \underline{\hspace{1.5cm}}$ fluid ounce. The total fill is approximately
normally $\underline{\hspace{1.5cm}}$ distributed with mean 72 and standard deviation .49.
b. Let T represent the total fill per six-pack. We wish to evaluate $P(T < 71)$.
72   Since T is approximately normally distributed with $\mu_T = \underline{\hspace{1.5cm}}$ and σ_T
.49 $= \underline{\hspace{1.5cm}}$,

$$P(T < 71) = P\left(\frac{T - 72}{.49} < \frac{71 - 72}{.49}\right)$$

$$= P(z < -2.04)$$

$$= .5000 - A(-2.04)$$

$$= .5000 - \underline{\hspace{2cm}} \qquad\qquad .4793$$

$$= \underline{\hspace{2cm}} \qquad\qquad .0207$$

Self-Correcting Exercises 5B

1. Given a random variable y with mean $\mu = 6$ and variance $\sigma^2 = 36$. A random sample of size $n = 40$ is taken.
   a. Describe the sampling distribution of $\bar{y}$.
   b. Calculate $P(\bar{y} > 7.5)$.
   c. Within what limits would we expect $\bar{y}$ to lie?
2. It is known that uric acid levels in normal adult males have an average of 5.7 mg/percent with a standard deviation of 1 mg/percent. A sample of 36 males is taken and the mean $\bar{y}$ is recorded.
   a. Within what limits would you expect $\bar{y}$ to lie?
   b. Calculate $P(\bar{y} > 6.1)$. If the sample of size 36 produces $\bar{y} = 6.1$, what would you conclude?

5.4 The Sampling Distribution of a Sample Proportion

For large values of n, the binomial probabilities

$$P(y) = \frac{n!}{y!(n-y)!}\, p^y q^{n-y}$$

are very tedious to compute. Is there an alternative to long computations? There is, as we will see.

For a binomial experiment consisting of n trials, let

$$
\begin{aligned}
&y_1 = 1 \quad \text{if trial one is a success}\\
&y_1 = 0 \quad \text{if trial one is a failure}\\[6pt]
&y_2 = 1 \quad \text{if trial two is a success}\\
&y_2 = 0 \quad \text{if trial two is a failure}
\end{aligned}
$$

.
.
.

$$
\begin{aligned}
&y_n = 1 \quad \text{if trial } n \text{ is a success}\\
&y_n = 0 \quad \text{if trial } n \text{ is a failure}
\end{aligned}
$$

p

pq

Central Limit; approximately; $np; npq$
large

$0; n;$ bell

95

4

2

Then y, the number of successes in n trials, can be thought of as a sum of n independent random variables each with mean equal to _____ and a variance equal to _____ . For

$$y = y_1 + y_2 + \ldots + y_n$$

the _____ _____ Theorem says this sum is _____ normally distributed with mean _____ and variance _____ . Hence when n is _____ , we can approximate the distribution of a binomial random variable with the distribution of a normal random variable whose mean and variance are identical to those for the binomial random variable. When can we reasonably apply the normal approximation? For small values of n and values of p close to 0 or 1, the binomial distribution will exhibit a "pile-up" around $y =$ _____ or $y =$ _____ . The data will not be _____ -shaped and the normal approximation will be poor. For a normal random variable, _____ % of the measurements will be within the interval $\mu \pm 2\sigma$. For $\mu = np$ and $\sigma = \sqrt{npq}$, the interval $np \pm 2\sqrt{npq}$ should be within the bounds of the binomial random variable y, or within the interval $(0, n)$, to obtain reasonably good approximations to the binomial probabilities.

To show how the normal approximation is used, let us consider a binomial random variable y with $n = 8$ and $p = \frac{1}{2}$ and attempt to approximate some binomial probabilities with a normal random variable having the same mean, $\mu = np$, and variance, $\sigma^2 = npq$, as the binomial y. In this case

$$\mu = np = 8(\tfrac{1}{2}) = \underline{\hspace{1.5cm}}$$

$$\sigma^2 = npq = 8(\tfrac{1}{2})(\tfrac{1}{2}) = \underline{\hspace{1.5cm}}$$

Note that the interval

$$\mu \pm 2\sigma = 4 \pm 2\sqrt{2} = (1.2, 6.8)$$

is contained within the interval $(0, 8)$; therefore our approximations should be adequate. Consider the following diagrammatic representation of the approximation, where $P(y)$ is the frequency distribution for the binomial random variable and $f(y)$ is the frequency distribution for the corresponding normal random variable y.

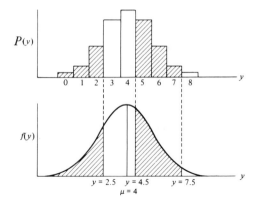

Example 5.6
Find $P(y < 3)$ using the normal approximation.

Solution
$P(y < 3)$ for the binomial random variable with mean $\mu = 4$ and $\sigma = \sqrt{2}$ corresponds to the shaded bars in the histogram over $y = 0, 1$, and 2. The approximating probability corresponds to the shaded area in the normal distribution with mean 4 and standard deviation $\sqrt{2}$ to the left of $y = 2.5$.
 We proceed as follows:

$$P(y < 3) \approx P(y < 2.5)$$

$$= P\left(\frac{y - 4}{\sqrt{2}} < \frac{2.5 - 4}{\sqrt{2}}\right)$$

$$= P(z < -1.06)$$

$$= .5000 - A(-1.06)$$

$$= .5000 - \underline{\hspace{1.5cm}}$$ .3554

$$= \underline{\hspace{1.5cm}}$$ .1446

Example 5.7
Find $P(5 \leqslant y \leqslant 7)$.

Solution
For the binomial random variable with mean 4 and standard deviation $\sqrt{2}$,
$P(5 \leqslant y \leqslant 7)$ corresponds to the shaded bars over $y = \underline{\hspace{1cm}}, \underline{\hspace{1cm}}$, 5; 6   (4)
and $\underline{\hspace{1cm}}$. This corresponds in turn to the shaded area for the approximating normal distribution with mean 4 and standard deviation $\sqrt{2}$ between $y =$ 7
$\underline{\hspace{1cm}}$ and $y = \underline{\hspace{1cm}}$. Therefore, 4.5; 7.5

$$P(5 \leqslant y \leqslant 7) \approx P(4.5 < y < 7.5)$$

$$= P\left(\frac{4.5 - 4}{\sqrt{2}} < \frac{y - 4}{\sqrt{2}} < \frac{7.5 - 4}{\sqrt{2}}\right)$$

$$= P(.35 < z < 2.47)$$

$$= A(2.47) - A(.35)$$

.4932; .1368

$$= \underline{\hspace{2cm}} - \underline{\hspace{2cm}}$$

.3564

$$= \underline{\hspace{2cm}}$$

Notice that we used $P(y < 2.5)$ to approximate the binomial probability $P(y < 3)$. In like manner we used $P(4.5 < y < 7.5)$ to approximate the binomial probability $P(5 \leqslant y \leqslant 7)$. The addition or subtraction of .5 is called the *correction for continuity* since we are approximating a discrete probability distribution with a probability distribution that is continuous. You may become confused as to whether .5 should be added or subtracted in the process of approximating binomial probabilities. A commonsense rule that always works is to examine the binomial probability statement carefully and determine which values of the binomial random variable are included in the statement. (Draw a picture if necessary.) The probabilities associated with these values correspond to the bars in the histogram centered over them. Locating the end points of the bars to be included determines the values needed for the approximating normal random variable.

Example 5.8
Suppose y is a binomial random variable with $n = 400$ and $p = .1$. Use the normal approximation to binomial probabilities to find the following:

a. $\quad P(y > 45)$.

b. $\quad P(y \leqslant 32)$.

c. $\quad P(34 \leqslant y \leqslant 46)$.

Solution
If y is binomial, then its mean and variance are

40

$$\mu = np = 400(.1) = \underline{\hspace{2cm}}$$

36

$$\sigma^2 = npq = 400(.1)(.9) = \underline{\hspace{2cm}}$$

a. To find $P(y > 45)$, we need the probabilities associated with the values 46,

$47, 48, \ldots, 400$. This corresponds to the bars in the binomial histogram beginning at _____ . Hence

45.5

$$P(y > 45) \approx P(y > 45.5)$$

$$= P\left(z > \frac{45.5 - 40}{6}\right)$$

$$= P(z > .92)$$

$$= \underline{\hspace{2cm}}$$

.1788

b. To find $P(y \leq 32)$, we need the probabilities associated with the values $0, 1, 2, \ldots$, up to and including $y = 32$. This corresponds to finding the area in the binomial histogram to the left of _____ . Hence

32.5

$$P(y \leq 32) \approx P(y < 32.5)$$

$$= P\left(z < \frac{32.5 - 40}{6}\right)$$

$$= P(z < \underline{\hspace{2cm}})$$

-1.25

$$= \underline{\hspace{2cm}}$$

.1056

c. To find $P(34 \leq y \leq 46)$, we need the probabilities associated with the values beginning at 34 up to and including 46. This corresponds to finding the area under the histogram between _____ and _____ . Hence

$33.5; 46.5$

$$P(34 \leq y \leq 46) \approx P(33.5 < y < 46.5)$$

$$= P\left(\frac{33.5 - 40}{6} < z < \frac{46.5 - 40}{6}\right)$$

$$= P(\underline{\hspace{2cm}} < z \underline{\hspace{2cm}})$$

$-1.08; 1.08$

$$= \underline{\hspace{2cm}}$$

.7198

Notice that the interval $\mu \pm 2\sigma$, or 40 ± 12, is well within the binomial range of 0 to 400, so that these approximate probabilities should be reasonably accurate.

Another statistic that is often used to describe a binomial population is $\hat{p}$, the *proportion* of trials in which a success is observed. In terms of previous notation,

$$\hat{p} = \frac{y}{n} = \frac{\text{number of successes in } n \text{ trials}}{n}$$

Recall that, for a binomial population, the proportion of successes in the population is defined as p. The sample proportion, $\hat{p}$, will be used to estimate or make inferences about p.

Using the fact that y, the number of successes can be thought of as a sum of n independent random variables, $y_1, y_2, \ldots, y_n$, the statistic $\hat{p} = y/n$ is equivalent to an _____ of these n random variables. The _____ _____ _____ assures us that $\hat{p}$ will be approximately normally distributed. The mean and standard deviation of $\hat{p}$ can be shown to be

$$\mu_{\hat{p}} = p \quad \text{and} \quad \sigma_{\hat{p}} = \sqrt{\frac{pq}{n}}$$

Example 5.9

Past records show that at a given college 20% of the students that began as psychology majors either changed their major or dropped out of school. An incoming class has 110 beginning psychology majors. What is the probability that at most 30% of these students leave the psychology program?

Solution

1. If $\hat{p}$ represents the proportion of students leaving the psychology program, with the probability of losing a student given as $p = .2$, then the required probability for $n = 110$ is

$$P(\hat{p} \leqslant .30)$$

2. To use the normal approximation, we need

$$\mu_{\hat{p}} = p = \underline{\hspace{2cm}}$$

$$\sigma_{\hat{p}} = \sqrt{\frac{pq}{n}} = \sqrt{\frac{.2(\underline{\hspace{1.5cm}})}{110}} = \sqrt{\underline{\hspace{1.5cm}}} = \underline{\hspace{1.5cm}}$$

We now proceed to approximate the probability required in part 1 by using a normal probability distribution with a mean of _____ and a standard deviation of _____.

3. Using the normal approximation, the value $\hat{p} = .30$ corresponds to a z value of

$$z = \frac{\hat{p} - p}{\sigma_{\hat{p}}} = \frac{.30 - .20}{.0381} = \underline{\hspace{1.5cm}}$$

The left margin contains the following notes:

average; Central
Limit Theorem

.2

.8; .0014545; .0381

.2
.0381

2.62

and

$$P(\hat{p} \leqslant .30) \approx P(z \leqslant \underline{\hspace{2cm}})$$

2.62

$$= .5000 + \underline{\hspace{2cm}}$$

.4956

$$= \underline{\hspace{2cm}}$$

.9956

Self-Correcting Exercises 5C

1. For a binomial experiment with $n = 10$ and $p = .7$, calculate $P(8 \leqslant y \leqslant 10)$ by
   a. using the binomial formula
   b. using the normal approximation
2. If the median income in a certain area is claimed to be $12,000, what is the probability that 37 or fewer of 100 randomly chosen wage earners from this area have incomes less than $12,000? Would the $12,000 figure seem reasonable if your sample actually contained 37 wage earners whose income was less than $12,000?
3. A large number of seeds from a certain species of flower are collected and mixed together in the following proportions according to the color of the flowers they will produce: 2 red, 2 white, 1 blue. If these seeds are mixed and then randomly packaged in bags containing about 100 seeds, what is the probability that a bag will contain the following:
   a. at most 50 "white" seeds
   b. at least 65 seeds that are not "white"
   c. at least 25 but at most 45 "white" seeds
4. In the population, a specific birth defect accounts for 10% of all birth defects. An investigator would like to know if this percentage is in fact higher if the age of the mother is over 40 years. Assume that the percentage of birth defects for births to mothers over 40 years is still 10%. If a sample of 100 births to mothers over 40 is observed, within what limits would you expect the proportion of babies with the specific birth defect to lie? If 18% of the babies are observed with the specific defect, what would you conclude?

EXERCISES

1. A sidewalk interviewer stopped three men who were walking together, asked their opinions on some topical subjects, and found their answers quite similar. Would you consider the interviewer's selection to be random in this case? Is it surprising that similar answers were given by these three men?
2. A preelection poll taken in a given city indicated that 40% of the voting public favored candidate *A*, 40% favored candidate *B*, and 20% were as yet un-

decided. If these percentages are true, in a random sample of 100 voters, what are the probabilities of the following events?

a. At most 50 voters in the sample prefer candidate A?

b. At least 65 voters in the sample prefer candidate B?

c. At least 25 but at most 45 voters in the sample prefer candidate B?

3. On a well-known college campus, the student automobile registration revealed that the ratio of small to large cars (as measured by engine displacement) is 2 to 1. If 72 car owners are chosen at random from the student body, find the probability that this group includes at most 46 owners of small cars.

4. The blood pressures for a population of individuals are approximately normally distributed with a mean of 110 and a variance of 49.

a. If a sample of 50 individuals is chosen randomly from this population, within what limits would you expect the sample mean, $\bar{y}$, to lie?

b. What is the probability that the sample mean will exceed 115?

5. In introducing a new breakfast sausage to the public, an advertising campaign claimed that 7 out of 10 shoppers would prefer these new sausages over other brands. Suppose 100 people are randomly chosen, and the advertiser's claim is true.

a. What is the probability that at most 65 people prefer the new sausages?

b. What is the probability that at least 80 people prefer the new sausages?

c. If only 60 people stated a preference for the new sausages, would this be sufficient evidence to indicate that the advertising claim is false and that, in fact, less than 7 out of 10 people would prefer the new sausages?

6. Graduate students applying for entrance to many universities must take a Miller Analogies Test. It is known that the test scores have a mean of 75 and a variance of 16. In 1973 one hundred students applied for entrance into graduate school in physics. Find the probability that the average score on these 100 tests is higher than 76.

Chapter 6

MAKING INFERENCES: ESTIMATION

6.1 Introduction

The objective of statistics is to make inferences about a _____,   population
based on information contained in a _____ . Since populations are   sample
described by numerical descriptive measures, called parameters of the population, we can make inferences about the population by making inferences about
its _____ . For example, one might want to estimate the effectiveness   parameters
of a new vaccine, in which case an inference must be made concerning its preven-
tion rate. In chapters 6 and 7 we will consider two methods for making inferences concerning population parameters: estimation and hypothesis testing.

Example 6.1

In an initial experiment to assess the merits of using a newly developed filling
material in bed pillows, 50 persons randomly selected from a group of volunteers agreed to test the new filling by actually using both the standard pillow and
one made with the new filling in their homes. To avoid biases that might influence the volunteer's decision, both pillows were covered with the same material.
One pillow carried the number "one" and the other the number "two." Only
the experimenter knew which number represented the standard and which represented the new material. After one week's use, each volunteer stated his or her
preference for one of the two pillows.

Let p be the probability that a volunteer would prefer the new pillow to the
standard. For a large hypothetical population of volunteers, p can also be described as the proportion of volunteers in the population who prefer the new
pillow to the standard. If an inference is to be made about p, two questions
could be asked.

1. What is the most likely value of p for the population from which we are sampling?
2. Does the new pillow have more desirable properties than the standard, and hence is it preferred more often than the standard?

The first question is one of predicting or estimating the population parameter p. The second is a question of testing an hypothesis about p. If there is no underlying difference between the new and standard pillow, then the probability that a volunteer would prefer the new pillow to the standard would be $p = \frac{1}{2}$. If, on the other hand, this is not true and the new pillow has more desirable properties than the standard, then p, the probability that a volunteer prefers the new pillow, would be greater than $\frac{1}{2}$. The objective of the test is to determine which of these two hypotheses about p is correct.

This chapter will be concerned with estimating two parameters:
1. μ, the mean of a population of continuous measurements
2. p, the parameter of a binomial population

The quantities to be used in making inferences will be sums or averages of the measurements in a random sample and consequently will possess frequency distributions in repeated sampling that are approximately _____ due to the _____ _____ Theorem.

Using the measurements in a sample to predict the value of one or more parameters of a population is called _____ . An _____ is a rule that tells us how to calculate an estimate of a parameter based on the information contained in a sample. We can give many different estimators for a particular population parameter. An estimator is often expressed in terms of a mathematical formula in which the estimate is a function of the sample measurements. For example, $\bar{y}$ is an *estimator* of the population parameter μ. If a sample of $n = 20$ pieces of aluminum cable is tested for strength and the mean of the sample is $\bar{y} = 100.7$, then 100.7 is an *estimate* of the population mean strength μ. The estimator of a parameter is usually designated by placing a "hat" over the parameter to be estimated. Thus an estimator of μ would be $\hat{\mu} = \bar{y}$.

Estimates of a population parameter can be made in two ways:
1. The measurements in the sample can be employed to calculate a single number that is the estimate of the population parameter. This is called a _____ estimate.
2. The measurements in the sample can also be used to calculate two points from which we acquire an estimate in the form of upper and lower limits within which the true value of the parameter is expected to lie. This type of estimate is called an _____ estimate since it defines an interval on the real line.

One of the most important concepts to grasp is that estimation as well as hypothesis testing is a two-step procedure. These steps are
1. making the inference, and
2. measuring its goodness.

A measure of the goodness of an inference is essential to enable the person

---

normal
Central Limit

estimation; estimator

point

interval

using the inference to measure its reliability. For example, we would wonder how close to the population parameter our estimate is expected to lie.

Rather than follow the section numbers exactly as they appear in your text, we have grouped certain topics together and will consider two more general sections: (1) point estimation and (2) interval estimation.

6.2 Point Estimation

In this section we will consider point estimation for the following two parameters:
1. μ, the mean of a population of continuous measurements
2. p, a binomial parameter

We assume, in both cases, that the samples are relatively large so that the estimators possess distributions in repeated sampling that are approximately normal due to the _____ _____ Theorem. The basic estimation problem is the same for both cases, and therefore we can discuss the problems in general by referring to the estimation of some population parameter, θ. Thus, θ might be either of the two parameters just mentioned.

Central Limit

To estimate the population parameter θ, a sample of size n consisting of the observations $y_1, y_2, \ldots, y_n$ is randomly drawn from the population and an estimate of θ is calculated using $\hat{\theta}$.
1. To estimate $\theta = \mu$, we use $\hat{\theta} = \bar{y}$.
2. To estimate $\theta = p$, we use

$$\hat{\theta} = \hat{p} = \frac{y}{n} = \frac{\text{number of successes}}{\text{number of trials}}$$

For each different random sample, a different value for $\hat{\theta}$ will be calculated. Hence, in repeated sampling, a sampling distribution for $\hat{\theta}$ will be generated and will possess the following properties:
1. The average (or mean) of the distribution of $\hat{\theta}$ is θ. In particular, the mean of the sampling distribution of $\bar{y}$ is _____ and the mean of the sampling distribution of $\hat{p}$ is _____.

μ
p

2. When n is large, the sampling distribution of $\hat{\theta}$ is approximately _____. Therefore, approximately 95% of the values of $\hat{\theta}$ will lie within two standard deviations of their mean, θ.

normal

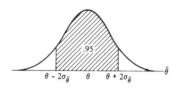

error of
estimation

$2\sigma_{\hat{\theta}}$

3. The symbol $\sigma_{\hat{\theta}}$ denotes the standard deviation of $\hat{\theta}$. Thus $\sigma_{\hat{\theta}}$ will be the standard deviation of the estimates generated by $\hat{\theta}$ in repeated sampling.

The measure of goodness of a particular estimate is the distance that it lies from the target θ. We call this distance, $|\hat{\theta} - \theta|$, the _____ _____ _____. The smaller the error of estimation, the better the estimate. Since θ is unknown it is not possible to exactly calculate the error of estimation. However, since $\hat{\theta}$ possesses the properties stated above, the probability is approximately .95 that the error of estimation will be less than _____. We often refer to $2\sigma_{\hat{\theta}}$ as the *bound* on the error of estimation. By this we mean that the error will be less than $2\sigma_{\hat{\theta}}$ with high probability (say, near .95).

Complete the following table, filling in the estimator and its standard deviation where required:

$\dfrac{\Sigma y}{n}$

$\dfrac{y}{n} \; ; \; \dfrac{\sqrt{pq}}{n}$

Parameter	Estimator	Standard Deviation
μ	$\bar{y} =$ _____	$\dfrac{\sigma}{\sqrt{n}}$
p	$\hat{p} =$ _____	_____

Notice that evaluation of the standard deviations given in the table may require values of parameters that are unknown. When the sample sizes are large, the sample estimates can be used to calculate an approximate standard deviation. As a rule of thumb, we will consider samples of size 30 or greater to be large samples for continuous populations. Samples from binomial populations will be considered large if np and nq are both greater than 10.

Example 6.2

The mean length of stay for patients in a hospital must be known in order to estimate the number of beds required. The length of stay, recorded for a sample of 400 patients at a given hospital, produced a mean and a standard deviation equal to 5.7 and 8.1 days, respectively. Give a point estimate for μ, the mean length of stay for patients entering the hospital, and place a bound of error on this estimate.

Solution

5.7

1. The point estimate for μ is $\bar{y} =$ _____.
2. The bound on the error of estimation is

$$2\sigma_{\bar{y}} = 2\,\frac{\sigma}{\sqrt{n}}$$

Since σ is unknown but $n \geqslant 30$, s can be used to estimate σ and the *approximate* bound on error is

$$2\frac{s}{\sqrt{n}} = 2\frac{8.1}{\sqrt{400}} = \underline{\hspace{2cm}}$$

.81

Example 6.3

Suppose that a researcher believes that a person's perception can be altered through suggestion. Under a controlled situation 50 objects were shown to each of two subjects and the subjects each estimated the distance to the object aloud. Unknown to subject B, subject A (who always responded first) was part of the experiment and was told to overestimate the distance for the first 25 objects and underestimate the distance for the last 25 objects. The experimenter found the number of times that subject B agreed with subject A in either overestimating or underestimating the true distance to be $y = 39$. Give a point estimate for p, the probability of agreement, and place a bound on the error of estimation.

Solution

1. The point estimate of p is

$$\hat{p} = \frac{y}{n} = \frac{}{50} = \underline{\hspace{2cm}}$$

39; 0.78

   That is, the subject B tends to agree with subject A's overestimation or underestimation _____ % of the time.

78

2. The bound on the error of estimation is $2\sigma_{\hat{p}} = 2\sqrt{pq/n}$. The quantities p and q are unknown. However, since n is large and $n\hat{p}$ and $n\hat{q}$ are both greater than 10, $\hat{p}$ and $\hat{q}$ may be substituted for p and q without too much error being introduced. The *approximate* bound on the error of estimation is

$$2\sqrt{\frac{\hat{p}\hat{q}}{n}} = 2\sqrt{\frac{}{50}} = 2\sqrt{\underline{\hspace{1.5cm}}}$$

.78 (.22); .003432

$$= 2(\underline{\hspace{1.5cm}}) = \underline{\hspace{1.5cm}}$$

.0586; .12

Example 6.4

Refer to example 6.3. Does it appear that A's suggestion is influencing B's response?

Solution

If suggestion does not influence B's response, then the probability of agreement on any one object would be $p = \frac{1}{2}$. If, on the other hand, this is not true and suggestion does influence B's response, then the probability of agreement, p, would be greater than $\frac{1}{2}$. Since our estimate of p is $\hat{p} = .78$ with bound on error equal to _____, the lower limit on possible values for p is $.78 - .12 = \underline{\hspace{1.5cm}}$. Hence, it is unlikely that $p = .50$. It would appear that A's suggestion (is, is not) influencing B's response.

.12; .66

is

Self-Correcting Exercises 6A

1. In standardizing an examination, the average score on the exam must be known in order to differentiate among examinees taking the examination. The scores recorded for a sample of 93 examinees yielded a mean and a standard deviation of 67.5 and 8.2, respectively. Estimate the true mean score for this examination and place bounds on the error of estimation.

2. Using the following data, give a point estimate with bound on error for the mortality in breast cancers where radical mastectomy was used as treatment.

    Number died: 31
    Number treated: 204

3. A physican wishes to estimate the proportion of accidents on the California freeway system that result in fatal injuries to at least one person. He randomly checks the files on 50 automobile accidents and finds that 8 resulted in fatal injuries. Estimate the true proportion of fatal accidents, and place bounds on the error of estimation.

4. In an experiment to assess the strength of the hunger drive in rats, 30 previously trained animals were deprived of food for 24 hours. At the end of the 24-hour period each animal was put into a cage where food was dispensed if the animal pressed a lever. The length of time the animal continued pressing the bar (although he was receiving no food) was recorded for each animal. If the data yielded a sample mean of 19.3 minutes with a standard deviation of 5.2 minutes, estimate the true mean time and place bounds on the error of estimation.

6.3 Interval Estimation

An interval estimator is a rule that tells us how to calculate two points based on information contained in a sample. The objective is to form a narrow interval that will enclose the parameter. As in the case of point estimation, we can form many interval estimators (rules) for estimating the parameter of interest. Not all intervals generated by an interval estimator will actually enclose the parameter. The probability that an interval estimate will enclose the parameter is called the

confidence coefficient

_____ _____.

Let $\hat{\theta}$ be a point estimator with average value θ, and suppose that $\hat{\theta}$ generates a normal distribution of estimates in repeated sampling. The mean of this distribution of estimates is _____ and the standard deviation is $\sigma_{\hat{\theta}}$. Then

θ

95

90

_____ % of the point estimates will lie within $1.96\sigma_{\hat{\theta}}$ of the parameter θ. Similarly, _____ % will lie in the interval $(\theta \pm 1.645\sigma_{\hat{\theta}})$.

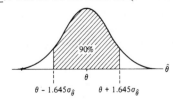

90%

θ

$\theta - 1.645\sigma_{\hat{\theta}}$ $\theta + 1.645\sigma_{\hat{\theta}}$

Suppose we were to construct an interval estimate by measuring the distance $1.645\sigma_{\hat{\theta}}$ on either side of $\hat{\theta}$. *Intervals constructed in this manner will enclose θ _____ % of the time* (see below).

90

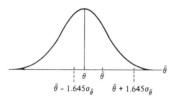

The general formula for a confidence interval for θ (where θ is either μ or p) is

$$\hat{\theta} \pm z\sigma_{\hat{\theta}}$$

The value of z is chosen depending on the desired degree of confidence.

Not all good interval estimators are constructed by measuring $z\sigma_{\hat{\theta}}$ on either side of the best point estimator, but this is true for the parameters μ and p. These confidence intervals are good for samples that are large enough to achieve approximate normality for the distribution of $\hat{\theta}$ and good approximations for unknown parameters appearing in $\sigma_{\hat{\theta}}$.

1. A confidence interval for μ is $\bar{y} \pm z\sigma/\sqrt{n}$. As a rule of thumb, the sample size n must be greater than or equal to _____ in order that s be a good approximation to σ.

30

2. A confidence interval for p is $(\hat{p} \pm z\sqrt{pq/n})$. As a rule of thumb, $n\hat{p}$ and $n\hat{q}$ must both be greater than _____ in order that $\hat{p}$ and $\hat{q}$ may be substituted for p and q in $\sigma_{\hat{p}}$.

10

Give the z values corresponding to the following confidence coefficients:

Confidence Coefficients	z
.95	1.96
.90	_____
.99	_____

1.645
2.58

Example 6.5

To construct a 90% confidence interval for the mean length of hospital stay, μ, based on the sample of $n = 400$ patients ($\bar{y} = 5.7$ and $s = 8.1$), we calculate

$$\bar{y} \pm z\sigma/\sqrt{n}$$

Using $z = 1.645$ and an estimate for σ given by $s = 8.1$, the interval estimate for the mean length of hospital stay is given as

$$5.7 \pm .67$$

More properly, we estimate that _____ $< \mu <$ _____ with 90% confidence.

5.03; 6.37

Example 6.6

An experimental rehabilitation technique employed on released convicts showed that 79 of a total of 121 men subjected to the technique pursued useful and crime-free lives for a three-year period following prison release. Find a 95% confidence interval for p, the probability that a convict subjected to the rehabilitation technique will follow a crime-free existence for at least three years after prison release.

Solution

The sampling described above satisfies the requirements of a binomial experiment consisting of $n = 121$ trials. In estimating the parameter p with a 95% confidence interval, we use the estimator

1.96

$$\hat{p} \pm \underline{\hspace{2cm}} \sqrt{pq/n}$$

Since p is unknown, the sample value $\hat{p}$ will be used in the approximation of $\sqrt{pq/n}$. Collecting pertinent information, we have

.65

1. $\hat{p} = \dfrac{y}{n} = \dfrac{79}{121} = \underline{\hspace{2cm}}$

2. $\sqrt{\dfrac{\hat{p}\hat{q}}{n}} = \sqrt{\dfrac{(.65)(.35)}{121}} = .04$

3. The interval estimate is given as

.08

$$.65 \pm 1.96(.04) \quad \text{or} \quad .65 \pm \underline{\hspace{2cm}}$$

.57; .73

4. We estimate that $\underline{\hspace{2cm}} < p < \underline{\hspace{2cm}}$ with 95% confidence.

Example 6.7

In assessing the effect of the color of food on taste preferences, 65 subjects were each asked to taste two samples of mashed potatoes, one of which was colored pink, the other its natural color. Although both samples were identical except for the pink color produced by the addition of a drop of tasteless food coloring, 53 of the subjects preferred the taste of the sample possessing its natural color. Estimate the true proportion of subjects who would apparently reject the pink potatoes on the basis of color alone with a 99% confidence interval.

Solution

1. Gathering the pertinent information required with $n = 65$ and $y = 53$,

.185; 2.58

$$\hat{p} = 53/65 = .815; \hat{q} = 1 - .815 = \underline{\hspace{2cm}}; z = \underline{\hspace{2cm}}$$

2. Using $\hat{p} \pm 2.58 \sqrt{\hat{p}\hat{q}/n}$, we find

$$.815 \pm 2.58 \sqrt{\underline{\hspace{2cm}}}$$

$$.815 \pm 2.58 \, (\underline{\hspace{2cm}})$$

$$.815 \pm \underline{\hspace{2cm}}$$

$$\frac{(.815)(.185)}{65}$$

.048

.124

Self-Correcting Exercises 6B

1. A random check of 50 savings accounts at the local city bank showed an average savings of $89.50 with a standard deviation of $25.10. Estimate the average savings in the accounts at this bank. Calculate 95% confidence limits for the mean savings in the bank's accounts.

2. In an attempt to update rates in a specific area, a fire insurance company randomly selects 50 fire insurance claims involving damage to one-family wooden frame dwellings with approximately 1500 square feet of living area. The average claim was found to be $8750 with a standard deviation of $3050. Estimate the true mean claim for structures of this type with a 95% confidence interval estimate.

3. Suppose it is necessary to estimate the percentage of students on the University of Florida campus who favor constitutional revision of the state constitution. In a random sample of 65 students, 30 stated that they were in favor of revision. Estimate the percentage of students favoring revision with a 99% confidence interval.

4. A sample of 39 cigarettes of a certain brand, tested for nicotine content, gave a mean of 22 milligrams and a standard deviation of 4 milligrams. Find a 90% confidence interval for the average nicotine content of this brand of cigarette.

5. In investigating the potential market for a new product within a given area, a market researcher asked 100 randomly chosen people to rank the new product together with four standard brands. Twenty-five people ranked the new product either first or second in a possible ranking from one to five. If p is the proportion of the population that would rank the new product either first or second, use the sample data to estimate p using a 99% confidence interval.

6.4 Summary

Estimation as a method of inference making has been discussed in this chapter. Point estimation and interval estimation for two parameters, μ and p, are used for large-sample situations.

To provide a brief summary of the preceding sections, complete the following tables.

a. Give the best estimator for each of the following parameters:

$\bar{y}$
$\hat{p}$

Parameter	Estimator
μ	_____
p	_____

b. Give the standard deviations for the following estimators:

$\dfrac{\sigma}{\sqrt{n}}$

$\sqrt{\dfrac{pq}{n}}$

Estimator	Standard Deviation
$\bar{y}$	_____
$\hat{p}$	_____

c. The exact values for standard deviations of estimators cannot usually be found because they are functions of unknown population parameters. Indicate the best approximations of the standard deviations for use in confidence intervals:

$\dfrac{s}{\sqrt{n}}$

$\sqrt{\dfrac{\hat{p}\hat{q}}{n}}$

$2\sigma_{\hat{\theta}}$
$\hat{\theta} \pm z\sigma_{\hat{\theta}}$

Estimator	Best Approximation of Standard Deviation
$\bar{y}$	_____
$\hat{p}$	_____

Bounds on error are then given as _____ or its approximation, while large-sample confidence intervals are given as _____, using the best approximation for unknown parameters in $\sigma_{\hat{\theta}}$.

EXERCISES

1. List the two essential elements of any inference-making procedure.
2. Describe the two types of estimators discussed in this chapter.
3. A bank was interested in estimating the average size of its savings accounts for a particular class of customer. If a random sample of 400 such accounts showed an average amount of $61.23 and a standard deviation of $18.20, place 90% confidence limits on the actual average account size.
4. If 36 measurements of the specific gravity of aluminum had a mean of 2.705 and a standard deviation of .028, construct a 99% confidence interval for the actual specific gravity of aluminum.

5. In a sample of 400 seeds, 240 germinate. Estimate the true germination percentage with a 95% confidence interval.
6. Refer to exercise 4. Estimate the specific gravity of aluminum and place bounds on the error of estimation. Compare these results to the results obtained in exercise 4. Can you explain the difference?
7. In a study to establish the absolute threshold of hearing, 70 male college freshmen were asked to participate. Each subject was seated in a soundproof room and a 150 Hz tone was presented at a large number of stimulus levels in a randomized order. The subject was instructed to press a button if he detected the tone. The mean for the group was 21.6 db with $s = 2.1$. Estimate the mean absolute threshold of all men 19–21 years of age and place bounds on the error of estimation.
8. A researcher classified his subjects as innately right-handed or left-handed by comparing thumb-nail widths. He took a sample of 400 men and found that 80 men could be classified as left-handed according to his criterion. Estimate p for all males with a 95% confidence interval, where p represents the probability a man tests to be left-handed.

Chapter   7

MAKING INFERENCES: TESTING HYPOTHESES

7.1   Introduction

In chapter 6 we presented estimation as an inferential technique. We developed both point and interval estimators for the binomial parameter p, and the mean μ of a population of continuous measurements.

We now turn our attention to a decision-making form of inference, hypothesis testing. In hypothesis testing, we formulate an hypothesis about a population in terms of its _____, and then, after observing a _____ drawn from this population, we decide whether our sample value could have come from the hypothesized population. We then accept or reject the hypothesized value. Hypothesis testing will be discussed for the case of a binomial parameter p, and for μ, the mean of a population of continuous measurements.

parameters; sample

7.2   A Statistical Test of an Hypothesis

A statistical test of an hypothesis consists of four parts:
1. _____ _____ , (H_0):   This is the hypothesis to be tested and gives hypothesized values for one or more population parameters.

   Null hypothesis

2. _____ or _____ _____ , (H_a):   This is the hypothesis against which H_0 is tested. We look for evidence in the sample that will cause us to reject H_0 in favor of H_a.

   Research
   alternative hypothesis

3. Test statistic: This function of the sample values extracts the information about the parameter contained in the sample. The observed value of the test statistic leads us to reject one hypothesis and accept the other.
4. Rejection region: Once the test statistic to be used is selected, the entire set of values that the statistic may assume is divided into two regions. The acceptance region consists of those values most likely to have arisen if H_0

were true. The rejection region consists of those values most likely to have arisen if H_a were true. If the observed value of the test statistic falls in the rejection region, H_0 is rejected; if it falls in the acceptance region, H_0 is accepted.

Our approach will be to draw a random sample from the population of interest and decide whether we will accept or reject an hypothesized value of the specified parameter. The decision will be made on the basis of whether the sample results are highly _____ and support the hypothesized value or are _____ and fail to support the hypothesized value. Our procedure is very similar to a court trial in which the accused is assumed innocent until proven guilty. In fact, our sample acts as the _____ for or against the accused. What we do is to compare the hypothesized value with reality. Let us illustrate how a test of an hypothesis is conducted.

probable

improbable

evidence

Example 7.1

A large orchard has averaged 140 pounds of apples per tree per year. A new fertilizer is tested to try to increase yield. Forty trees are randomly selected and the mean and standard deviation of yield are $\bar{y} = 143.2$ and $s = 9.4$. Do the data indicate a significant increase in yield?

Solution

If there is no increase in the average yield for fertilized trees, then the average value μ of the hypothetical population of fertilized trees from which we have obtained a random sample is $\mu = 140$. If, on the other hand, this is not true and the fertilizer tends to increase yield, then μ, the mean yield for fertilized trees, would be greater than 140. Since the researcher is interested in detecting an increase in yield, the statement $\mu > 140$ is the _____ or _____ hypothesis, while the statement $\mu = 140$ is the _____ _____.

research

alternative; null

hypothesis

Assuming that there is no increase in the average yield for fertilized trees, it would be extremely unlikely in a sample of $n = 40$ trees to observe certain values of $\bar{y}$. Since $\bar{y}$ has an approximate normal distribution with $\mu_{\bar{y}} = 140$ and

1.486

$$\sigma_{\bar{y}} \approx \frac{s}{\sqrt{n}} = \frac{9.4}{\sqrt{40}} = \underline{\quad\quad}$$

we can calculate the probability of observing a particular value of $\bar{y}$ or something even more extreme. For example, suppose that $\bar{y} = 150$. This is a highly unlikely event since

$$P(\bar{y} > 150) = P\left(z > \frac{150 - 140}{1.486}\right)$$

6.73; 0

$$= P(z > \underline{\quad\quad}) \approx \underline{\quad\quad}$$

The observance of $\bar{y} = 141$, however, is not so unlikely, since

$$P(\bar{y} > 141) = P\left(z > \underline{\qquad}\right)$$

$$\begin{array}{r} 141 - 140 \\ \hline 1.486 \end{array}$$

$$= P(z > \underline{\qquad})$$

.67

$$= .5 - \underline{\qquad} = \underline{\qquad}$$

.2486; .2514

In conducting a test of hypothesis, the possible outcomes for $\bar{y}$ are divided into those for which we agree to reject the null hypothesis [those values of $\bar{y}$ that are much (greater, less) than $\mu = 140$] and those for which we accept the null hypothesis [those values of $\bar{y}$ that are (close to, far away from) $\mu = 140$.]

greater
close to

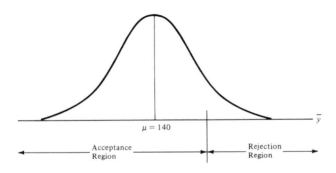

There are many possible rejection regions available to the experimenter. A sound choice among various reasonable rejection regions can be made after considering the possible errors that can be made in a test of an hypothesis.

The following table is called a *decision table* and looks at the two possible states of nature (H_0 and H_a) and the two possible decisions in a test of an hypothesis. Fill in the missing entries as either "correct" or "error":

Null Hypothesis	Decision	
	Reject H_0	Accept H_0
True	_____	correct
False	correct	_____

error
error

An error of type I is made when we reject H_0 when H_0 is (true, false). An error of type II is made when we fail to reject H_0 when H_a is (true, false). In considering a statistical test of an hypothesis, it is essential to know the probabilities of committing errors of type I and type II when the test is used. We define

true
true

$$\alpha = P(\text{type I error}) = P(\text{reject } H_0 \text{ when } H_0 \text{ true})$$

$$\beta = P(\text{type II error}) = P(\text{accept } H_0 \text{ when } H_a \text{ true})$$

For this example, suppose we set the region $\bar{y} > 142$ as the rejection region.

1. If H_0 is true and $\mu = 140$,

$$\alpha = P(\text{reject } H_0 | H_0 \text{ true})$$

$$= P(\bar{y} > 142) = P\left(z > \frac{142 - 140}{1.486}\right)$$

1.35; .4115

$$= P(z > \underline{\hspace{2cm}}) = .5 - \underline{\hspace{2cm}}$$

.0885

$$= \underline{\hspace{2cm}}$$

2. If H_0 is false and $\mu = 145$,

$$\beta = P(\text{accept } H_0 | H_a \text{ true})$$

$$= P(\bar{y} < 142 | \mu = 145)$$

$$= P\left(z < \frac{142 - 145}{1.486}\right)$$

−2.02; .4783

$$= P(z < \underline{\hspace{2cm}}) = .5 - \underline{\hspace{2cm}}$$

.0217

$$= \underline{\hspace{2cm}}$$

Notice that β is a function of H_a, since by definition,

$$\beta = P(\text{accepting } H_0 | H_a \text{ true})$$

By saying H_a is true, we mean that the true value of the population parameter is that given by H_a, and β is computed using that value.

Consider a second rejection region, $\bar{y} > 144$. This rejection region is (larger,

smaller

smaller) than the first region.

1. If H_0 is true, and $\mu = 140$,

$$\alpha = P(\text{reject } H_0 | H_0 \text{ true})$$

$$= P(\bar{y} > 144 | \mu = 140)$$

$$= P\left(z > \underline{\hspace{2cm}}\right) \qquad \frac{144 - 140}{1.486}$$

$$= P(z > 2.69)$$

$$= .5 - .4964 = .0036$$

2. If H_0 is false and $\mu = 145$,

$$\beta = P(\text{accept } H_0 | H_a \text{ true})$$

$$= P(\bar{y} < 144 | \mu = 145)$$

$$= P\left(z < \underline{\hspace{2cm}}\right) \qquad \frac{144 - 145}{1.486}$$

$$= P(z < -.67)$$

$$= .5 - \underline{\hspace{1.5cm}} = \underline{\hspace{1.5cm}} \qquad .2486; .2514$$

Notice that both α and β depend on the rejection region employed and that when the sample size n is fixed, α and β are inversely related: as one increases, the other _____. Increasing the sample size provides more informa-   decreases
tion on which to make the decision and will reduce the probability of a type II error. Since these two quantities measure the risk of making an incorrect de-
cision, the experimenter chooses reasonable values for α and β and then chooses
the rejection region and sample size accordingly. Since experimenters have found
that a 1-in-20 chance of a type I error is usually tolerable, common practice is to
choose $\alpha \leqslant$ _____ and a sample size n large enough to provide the desired   .05
control of the type II error.

7.3 A Large-Sample Test of an Hypothesis

As in previous sections, the parameter of interest (μ or p) will be referred to as θ.
If a point estimator $\hat{\theta}$ exists which is normally distributed with average value θ,
we can employ $\hat{\theta}$ as a test statistic to test the hypothesis $H_0: \theta = \theta_0$.
     If H_a states that $\theta > \theta_0$, that is, the value of the parameter is greater than that
given by H_0, then the sample value for $\hat{\theta}$ should reflect this fact and be (larger,   larger
smaller) than a value of $\hat{\theta}$ when sampling from a population whose mean is θ_0.

critical value

Hence we would reject H_0 for large values of $\hat{\theta}$. "Large" can be interpreted as too many standard deviations to the right of the mean θ_0. The value of $\hat{\theta}$ selected to separate the acceptance and rejection regions is called the

_____ _____ of the test statistic.

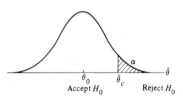

$\hat{\theta}_c$ in the diagram represents the critical value of $\hat{\theta}$ and the shaded area to the right of $\hat{\theta}_c$ is equal to _____. This is a one-tailed statistical test.

α

A similar picture could have been used with the critical value of $\hat{\theta}$ to the left of the mean for testing $H_0: \theta = \theta_0$ against $H_a: \theta$ _____ θ_0. Then we would reject for values of $\hat{\theta}$ lying too many standard deviations to the left of

<

one-tailed

θ_0 (resulting in a _____-_____ test in the left tail) and would reject H_0 for small values of $\hat{\theta}$.

two

A third type of alternative hypothesis would be $H_a: \theta \neq \theta_0$, where we seek departures either greater or less than θ_0. This results in a _____-tailed statistical test.

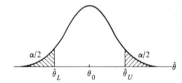

In order that the probability of a type I error be equal to α, two critical values of $\hat{\theta}$ must be found, one having area $\alpha/2$ to its right ($\hat{\theta}_U$) and one having area $\alpha/2$ to its left ($\hat{\theta}_L$). H_0 will be rejected if $\hat{\theta} \geq \hat{\theta}_U$ or $\hat{\theta} \leq \hat{\theta}_L$.

Since the estimator $\hat{\theta}$ is normally distributed, we can standardize the normal variable $\hat{\theta}$ by converting the distance that $\hat{\theta}$ departs from θ_0 to z (the number of standard deviations to the left or right of the mean). Thus we will use z as the test statistic. The four elements of the test are as follows:

1. $H_0: \theta = \theta_0$

2. One of the three alternatives:

    a. $H_a: \theta > \theta_0$ (right-tailed)

    b. $H_a: \theta < \theta_0$ (left-tailed)

    c. $H_a: \theta \neq \theta_0$ (two-tailed)

3. Test statistic z, where

$$z = \frac{\hat{\theta} - \theta_0}{\sigma_{\hat{\theta}}}$$

4. Rejection region: Let z_a be a value of z having area a to its right.
   a. For H_a: $\theta > \theta_0$,

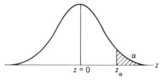

Reject H_0 if $z > z_\alpha$.

   b. For H_a: $\theta < \theta_0$,

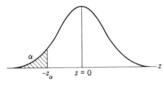

Reject H_0 if $z < -z_\alpha$.

   c. For H_a: $\theta \neq \theta_0$,

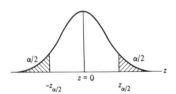

Reject H_0 if $z > z_{\alpha/2}$
or $z < -z_{\alpha/2}$
$(|z| > z_{\alpha/2})$

We now apply this test of an hypothesis.

Example 7.2

Test of a population mean μ. Test the hypothesis at the $\alpha = .05$ level, that a population mean $\mu = 10$ against the hypothesis that $\mu \neq 10$ if, for a sample of 81 observations, $\bar{y} = 12$ and $s = 3.2$. Note the following:

a. $\theta = \mu$ d. $\sigma_{\hat{\theta}} = \sigma/\sqrt{n}$

b. $\theta_0 = \mu_0 = 10$ e. $\alpha = .05$

c. $\hat{\theta} = \bar{y}$

Solution

Since σ is unknown, use s, the sample standard deviation, as its approximation. Then the elements of the test are as follows:

1. H_0: $\mu = 10$

2. H_a: $\mu \neq 10$

3. Test statistic:

$$z = \frac{\bar{y} - \mu_0}{\sigma/\sqrt{n}} \quad \text{(using } s \text{ if } \sigma \text{ is unknown)}$$

4. Rejection region:

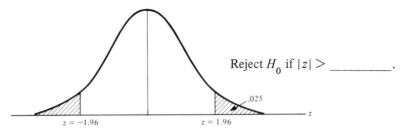

1.96

Reject H_0 if $|z| > \underline{\hspace{2cm}}$.

.025

$z = -1.96$ $z = 1.96$

Having defined the test, calculate z.

12

3.2

$$z = \frac{\bar{y} - \mu_0}{s/\sqrt{n}} = \frac{\underline{\hspace{1cm}} - 10}{\underline{\hspace{1cm}}/\sqrt{81}} = \frac{2}{.356} = 5.62$$

reject

Since $z = 5.62 > 1.96$, the decision is (reject, do not reject) H_0 with $\alpha = .05$.

Example 7.3
Test of a binomial p.   Consider example 6.7 in the context of a test of hypothesis. In assessing the effect of the color of food on taste preferences, 65 subjects were each asked to taste two samples of mashed potatoes, one of which was colored pink, the other its natural color. Although both samples were identical except for the pink color produced by the addition of a drop of tasteless food coloring, 53 of the subjects preferred the taste of the sample possessing its natural color. Does this indicate that subjects tend to be adversely affected by the pink color? Test at the $\alpha = .01$ level of significance.

Solution
In this problem, with $p = P$ (choose natural color), we have the following:

a. $\theta = p$

d. $\sigma_{\hat{\theta}} = \sqrt{p_0 q_0/n}$

½

b. $\theta_0 = p_0 = \underline{\hspace{2cm}}$

.01

c. $\hat{\theta} = \hat{p} = y/n$

e. $\alpha = \underline{\hspace{2cm}}$

Note that p_0 and q_0 are used in $\sigma_{\hat{p}}$ since we are testing $H_0: p = p_0$. The elements of the test are as follows:

1. $H_0: \; p = \frac{1}{2}$

2. $H_a: \; p > \frac{1}{2}$

3. Test statistic:

$$z = \frac{\hat{p} - p_0}{\sqrt{p_0 q_0 / n}}$$

4. Rejection region:

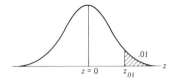

Reject H_0 if $z > $ _____.   2.33

To calculate z, we need $\hat{p} = y/n = 53/65 = .815$. Then

$$z = \frac{.815 - \underline{\hspace{1cm}}}{\sqrt{.5(.5)/65}} = \frac{.315}{.062} = 5.08$$

.500

Since $z = 5.08 > 2.33$ we (reject, do not reject) H_0 and conclude that color (does, does not) adversely affect a subject's choice.

reject
does

Example 7.4
Refer to example 7.1. Using $\alpha = .05$, set up a formal test of hypothesis to test the researcher's claim.

Solution

1. $H_0: \; \mu = 140$

2. $H_a: \; \mu > 140$

3. Test statistic:

$$z = \frac{\bar{y} - \mu_0}{\sigma/\sqrt{n}} \quad \text{(using } s \text{ if } \sigma \text{ is unknown)}$$

4. Rejection region:

1.645

1.645

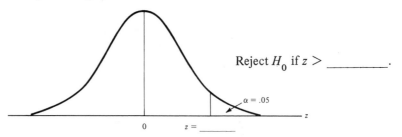

Reject H_0 if $z >$ _____.

$\alpha = .05$

$0 \qquad z =$ _____

Having defined the test, calculate z.

143.2

$$z = \frac{y - \mu_0}{\sigma/\sqrt{n}} \approx \frac{\text{_____} - 140}{9.4/\sqrt{40}}$$

3.2

2.15

1.486

$$= \frac{\text{_____}}{\text{_____}} = \text{_____}$$

2.15; reject

does

Since $z =$ _____ > 1.645, the decision is to (reject, not reject) H_0 with $\alpha =$ .05. The new fertilizer (does, does not) increase yield.

Self-Correcting Exercises 7A

1. A machine shop is interested in determining a measure of the current year's sales revenue in order to compare it with known results from last year. From the 9682 sales invoices for the current year to date, the management randomly selected $n = 400$ invoices and from each recorded y, the sales revenue per invoice. Using the following data summary, test the hypothesis that the mean revenue per invoice is $3.35, the same as last year, versus the alternative hypothesis that the mean revenue per invoice is different from $3.35, with $\alpha = .05$.

Data Summary		
$n = 400$	$\Sigma y = \$1{,}264.40$	$\Sigma y^2 = 4{,}970.3282$

2. A physician found 480 men and 420 women among 900 patients admitted to a hospital with a certain disease. Is this consistent with the hypothesis that in the population of patients hospitalized with this disease, half the cases are male? (Use $\alpha = .01$.)

3. The board of directors of a particular company is considering the possible merger of their company with another. If 34 shareholders in a random sample of 65 shareholders stated that they were in favor of the merger, test the hypothesis that a majority of the stockholders favor merger (the proportion favoring merger is greater than .5). (Use $\alpha = .05$.)

4. In a manufacturing plant employing a double inspection procedure, the first inspector is expected to miss an average of 25 defective items per day with a standard deviation of 3 items. If the first inspector has missed an average of 29 defectives per day based upon the last 30 working days, is he working up to company standards? (Use $\alpha = .01$.)

7.4 The Level of Significance of a Statistical Test

The structure of a statistical test of hypothesis can be summarized as follows:
1. State the null and _____ (or _____) hypotheses. | research; alternative
2. Choose a test statistic.
3. Choose a value of α and, depending on the nature of the alternative hypothesis, establish a one- or two-tailed rejection region for which the α level is approximately the level chosen.
4. Perform the experiment, calculate the test statistic and come to a conclusion based on the observed value of the test statistic. If the value of the test statistic falls in the rejection region we _____ the null hypothesis | reject
in favor of the alternative hypothesis. If the value of the test statistic is not in the rejection region we (can, cannot) reject the null hypothesis in favor of | cannot
the alternative hypothesis.

  One difficulty in utilizing the approach outlined above is that the choice of the α level is to some extent subjective. Another researcher may disagree with your conclusions regarding the research hypothesis because he or she does not agree with your choice of the α level. The _____ _____ | level of
_____ or p value for an observed value of the test statistic is the | significance
smallest α value for which the null hypothesis could be rejected. In using the rare-event philosophy, we reject the null hypothesis in favor of the alternative whenever the total probability of the observed value of the test statistic and any rarer event is _____. | small

  Consider the problem discussed in example 7.4. In that problem we tested $H_0: \mu = 140$ versus $H_a: \mu > 140$ based on an observed value of $\bar{y} = 143.2$. Since this is a one-tailed test and "large" values of $\bar{y}$ belong in the rejection region, the smallest rejection region that contains $\bar{y}$ is the region $\bar{y} \geqslant 143.2$. The p value associated with this observation is therefore

$$p \text{ value} = P(\bar{y} \geqslant \underline{\hspace{1.5cm}})$$ | 143.2

$$= P\left(z \geqslant \frac{143.2 - 140}{9.4/\sqrt{40}}\right)$$

$$= P(z > 2.15)$$

$$= .5 - .4842$$

$$= \underline{\hspace{1.5cm}}$$ | .0158

.0158; is

Thus any researcher who would specify an α value greater than or equal to _____ would conclude that there (is, is not) sufficient evidence to accept the research hypothesis.

The significance-level approach to hypothesis testing does not require specifying an α level before the analysis is undertaken. Rather, the degree of disagreement with the null hypothesis is quantified by the calculation of the

p value

_____ _____, which is used to make decisions regarding the research hypothesis.

Example 7.5

An experimenter has prepared a drug-dose level which he claims will induce sleep for at least 80 percent of people suffering from insomnia. After examining the dosage we feel that his claims regarding the effectiveness of his dosage are inflated. In an attempt to disprove his claim we administer his prescribed dosage to 50 insomniacs and observe that $y = 37$ have had sleep induced by the drug dose. Is there enough evidence to refute his claim?

Solution

1. The hypothesis to be tested is

$$H_0: \quad p = .8 \quad \text{versus}$$

$$H_a: \quad p < .8$$

2. The test statistic is $\hat{p}$, the proportion of insomniacs in which the drug dose induced sleep, or equivalently,

$$z = \frac{\hat{p} - p_0}{\sqrt{p_0 q_0 / n}}$$

small

negative

3. Since "small" values of $\hat{p}$ (or negative values of z) are expected when H_a is true, the rejection region should include the (small, large) values of $\hat{p}$. In terms of z, the rejection region should include large (positive, negative) values of z.

.74

4. For this example, $\hat{p} = y/n = 37/50 =$ _____. Equivalently,

$$z = \frac{\hat{p} - p_0}{\sqrt{p_0 q_0 / n}} = \frac{.74 - .80}{\sqrt{.80(.20)/50}}$$

.0032; –1.06

$$= \frac{-.06}{\sqrt{\underline{\hspace{1cm}}}} = \underline{\hspace{1.5cm}}$$

.74

$\leqslant .74; \leqslant -1.06$

The smallest rejection region that includes the observed value ($\hat{p} =$ _____) is $\hat{p}$ _____ or z _____. Hence, the p value associated with this observation is

p value $= P(\hat{p} \leqslant .74) = P(z \leqslant -1.06)$

$$= .5 - .3554$$

$$= \underline{\hspace{2cm}}$$ | .1446

5. The conclusion of any researcher who would choose an _____ value | α
($\leqslant, \geqslant$) .1446 would be that there (is, is not) enough evidence to support re- | $\geqslant$; is
jecting the null hypothesis ($p = $ _____) in favor of the alternative | .8
hypothesis (p _____). In the language of this problem, we would con- | $< .8$
clude that there (is, is not) enough evidence to indicate that the effectiveness | is
of the dosage has been exaggerated. However, since most researchers would
not find an α level as large as .1446 acceptable, our conclusion would be that
the value $y = 37$ (does, does not) provide enough evidence to reject the null | does not
hypothesis.

Example 7.6
Calculate the level of significance for the data in example 7.2.

Solution
The hypothesis to be tested is

$$H_0: \quad \mu = 10$$

$$H_a: \quad \mu \neq 10$$

This is a (one, two) -tailed test and the observed value of $\bar{y}$ was $\bar{y} = $ _____, | two; 12
or equivalently,

$$z = \frac{\bar{y} - \mu_0}{\sigma/\sqrt{n}} \approx \underline{\hspace{2cm}}$$ | 5.62

This value of the test statistic is in the (upper, lower) tail of the distribution if the | upper
null hypothesis is true. The collection of all values of z as rare or rarer than
$z = 5.62$ has probability $P(z \geqslant 5.62)$. Since the value $z = 5.62$ is not given in
Table 1 of the appendix, we can say only that the probability of interest is
(less than, greater than) that given for the last tabled entry. That is, | less than

$$P(z \geqslant 5.62) \text{ is less than } P(z \geqslant 3.09)$$

$$= .5 - \underline{\hspace{2cm}} = \underline{\hspace{2cm}}$$ | .4990; .001

This probability accounts for only the values of $\bar{y}$ in the upper tail of the distribution. There would be values of $\bar{y}$ which are equally as rare in the lower tail of
the distribution. In order to account for these realizations, the significance level
is calculated by _____ the value found above, so that | doubling

.001; .002

$\geqslant$

less

null
one
twice

$$p \text{ value} < 2(\underline{\hspace{2cm}}) = \underline{\hspace{2cm}}$$

Thus, for any researcher specifying an α value $(\geqslant, \leqslant)$ .002, the conclusion would be to accept the alternative hypothesis, $\mu \neq 10$.

In summary, the procedure used to determine levels of significance is as follows:

1. Look at the alternative hypothesis. If it is an upper-tail alternative, list all values of the test statistic greater than or equal to the value observed. If it is a lower-tail alternative, list all values of the test statistic _____ than or equal to the value observed. If it is a two-tailed alternative, determine which tail of the distribution contains the observed value and list all values as rare or rarer than the observed value that are in that tail.

2. Calculate the probability of getting a value of the test statistic in the collection of values given in part (1) assuming the _____ hypothesis is true. If the test is _____-tailed, this is the p value.

3. If the test is two-tailed, the p value is _____ the probability calculated in (2).

Self-Correcting Exercises 7B

1. Refer to exercise 1, Self-Correcting Exercises 7A. Give the level of significance for the test and interpret your results.

2. Refer to exercise 3, Self-Correcting Exercises 7A. Give the level of significance for the test and interpret your results.

3. Suppose it is hypothesized that $p = .1$. Test this hypothesis against the alternative that $p < 0.1$ if the number of successes is $y = 8$ in a sample of $n = 100$. Give the level of significance for the test and make a decision based on the p value.

EXERCISES

1. What are the four essential elements of a statistical test of an hypothesis?

2. Assume that a certain set of "early returns" in an election is actually a random sample of size 400 from the voters in that election. If 225 of the voters in the sample voted for candidate A, could we asset with $\alpha = .01$ that candidate A has won?

3. Refer to exercise 2 and give the level of significance for the test. Interpret your results.

4. A grocery store operator claims that the average waiting time at a checkout counter is 3.75 minutes. To test this claim, a random sample of 30 observations was taken. Test the operator's claim at the 5% level of significance, using the sample data shown below.

	Waiting Time in Minutes			
3	4	3	4	1
1	0	5	3	2
4	3	1	2	0
3	2	0	3	4
1	3	2	1	3
2	4	2	5	2

5. Refer to exercise 4 and give the level of significance for the test. Interpret your results.

6. In a maze running study, a rat is run in a T maze and the result of each run recorded. A reward in the form of food is always placed at the right exit. If learning is taking place, the rat will choose the right exit more often than the left. If no learning is taking place, the rat should randomly choose either exit. Suppose that the rat is given $n = 100$ runs in the maze and that he chooses the right exit $y = 64$ times. Would you conclude that learning is taking place? Give the level of significance of the test and make a decision based on the p value.

Chapter   8
COMPARISONS

8.1 Introduction

Chapters 2 through 7 have been concerned with statistics, the science of making inferences about a population based on information contained in a sample, as it relates to a single population of measurements of interest to the experimenter. In particular, we have considered two types of populations:
1. Binomial populations
2. Populations of continuous measurements
For these two types of populations we have considered a single random sample of size n, and have made inferences about the parameters p and μ using, respectively, the sample statistics

$$\hat{p} = \underline{\hspace{2cm}} \quad \text{and} \quad \bar{y} = \underline{\hspace{2cm}}$$

$$\frac{y}{n} ; \frac{\Sigma y}{n}$$

In practice, an experimenter is concerned with two populations; and in general, is interested in knowing whether or not these populations have the same location parameters. For two binomial populations, this involves a comparison of p_1 and p_2, while for two populations of continuous measurements, this involves a comparison of $(\mu_1 - \mu_2)$.

Example 8.1
A researcher is interested in the effect of vitamin C on the average cholesterol level in the human body. He designs an experiment in which two groups of people will be placed on a specified diet for a given length of time. One group's diet will be supplemented with a particular dose of vitamin C, while the other group's diet will not. The researcher is interested in measuring the difference in the average cholesterol levels for the two groups.

Example 8.2

A researcher at a large metropolitan hospital is recording the number of patients admitted for any type of heart ailment. She would like to know whether there is a difference in the percentage of men and women admitted to the hospital for any type of heart ailment.

In both of the above situations, the experimenter is considering two populations, which will be denoted as Population 1 or Population 2. These populations will be either (1) binomial populations or (2) populations consisting of continuous measurements. This chapter will be concerned with making inferences about the following parameters:

1. $(\mu_1 - \mu_2)$, the difference between the means for two populations of continuous measurements.
2. $(p_1 - p_2)$, the difference in the parameters for two binomial populations.

We will make inferences in one of three ways:

1. By estimating the value of the parameter with a point estimate and giving a bound on the error of estimation
2. By estimating the value of the parameter with a confidence interval
3. By testing an hypothesis about the value of the parameter

As in chapters 6 and 7, we have grouped certain topics together rather than follow the section numbers exactly as they appear in your text.

8.2 The Sampling Distribution of the Difference Between Two Sample Statistics

Consider two populations, 1 and 2, from which we select two independent random samples of size n_1 and n_2, respectively. Sample statistics will be calculated for each of the two samples. In general, denote these sample statistics by y_1 and y_2. We will use the following theorem, which gives the sampling distribution for the difference, $(y_1 - y_2)$, in two specific situations.

Theorem 8.1: If two independent random variables y_1 and y_2 are normally distributed with means μ_1 and μ_2 and variances σ_1^2 and σ_2^2, respectively, then the difference $(y_1 - y_2)$ will be normally distributed with mean $(\mu_1 - \mu_2)$ and variance $(\sigma_1^2 + \sigma_2^2)$.

Case I: The Sampling Distribution of $\bar{y}_1 - \bar{y}_2$

If samples of size n_1 and n_2 are randomly and independently selected from two continuous populations with means μ_1 and μ_2, respectively, a statistic which can be formed in order to make inferences about the difference $(\mu_1 - \mu_2)$ is

$(\bar{y}_1 - \bar{y}_2)$; 30

Central Limit

normally; μ_1

_____ . If n_1 and n_2 are both larger than _____, the

_____ _____ Theorem allows us to make the following

two statements:

1. $\bar{y}_1$ is approximately _____ distributed with mean $\mu_{\bar{y}_1}$ = _____ and variance

$$\sigma^2_{\bar{y}_1} = \underline{\hspace{3cm}}$$

$$\frac{\sigma^2_1}{n_1}$$

2. $\bar{y}_2$ is approximately _____ distributed with mean $\mu_{\bar{y}_2} = $ _____ and variance

normally; μ_2

$$\sigma^2_{\bar{y}_2} = \underline{\hspace{3cm}}$$

$$\frac{\sigma^2_2}{n_2}$$

Finally, using theorem 8.1, $(\bar{y}_1 - \bar{y}_2)$ will be approximately normally distributed with mean

$$\mu_{\bar{y}_1 - \bar{y}_2} = \mu_1 - \mu_2$$

and variance

$$\sigma^2_{\bar{y}_1 - \bar{y}_2} = \frac{\sigma^2_1}{n_1} + \frac{\sigma^2_2}{n_2}$$

The standard deviation of $\bar{y}_1 - \bar{y}_2$ is

$$\sigma_{\bar{y}_1 - \bar{y}_2} = \sqrt{\underline{\hspace{3cm}}}$$

$$\frac{\sigma^2_1}{n_1} + \frac{\sigma^2_2}{n_2}$$

Case II: The Sampling Distribution of $\hat{p}_1 - \hat{p}_2$.
If samples of size n_1 and n_2 are independently drawn from two binomial populations with parameters p_1 and p_2, respectively, a statistic that can be formed in order to make inferences about the difference $(p_1 - p_2)$ is _____ , where

$$(\hat{p}_1 - \hat{p}_2)$$

$$\hat{p}_1 = \frac{y_1}{n_1} = \frac{\text{number of successes in sample 1}}{\text{number of trials in sample 1}}$$

and

$$\hat{p}_2 = \frac{y_2}{n_2} = \frac{\text{number of successes in sample 2}}{\text{number of trials in sample 2}}$$

As long as $n_1 p_1$, $n_2 p_2$, $n_1 q_1$, and $n_2 q_2$ are all greater than or equal to

10; Central Limit

normally

p_1

$\dfrac{p_1 q_1}{n_1}$

normally

p_2

$\dfrac{p_2 q_2}{n_2}$

$p_1 - p_2$

$\dfrac{p_1 q_1}{n_1} + \dfrac{p_2 q_2}{n_2}$

_____ , the _____ _____ Theorem allows us to make the following two statements:

1. $\hat{p}_1$ is approximately _____ distributed with mean

$$\mu_{\hat{p}_1} = \underline{\qquad}$$

and variance

$$\sigma^2_{\hat{p}_1} = \underline{\qquad}$$

2. $\hat{p}_2$ is approximately _____ distributed with mean

$$\mu_{\hat{p}_2} = \underline{\qquad}$$

and variance

$$\sigma^2_{\hat{p}_2} = \underline{\qquad}$$

Using theorem 8.1, the sampling distribution of $(\hat{p}_1 - \hat{p}_2)$ is approximately normal with mean

$$\mu_{\hat{p}_1 - \hat{p}_2} = \underline{\qquad}$$

and variance

$$\sigma^2_{\hat{p}_1 - \hat{p}_2} = \underline{\qquad}$$

The standard deviation of $(\hat{p}_1 - \hat{p}_2)$ is

$$\sigma_{\hat{p}_1 \hat{p}_2} = \sqrt{\frac{p_1 q_1}{n_1} + \frac{p_2 q_2}{n_2}}$$

Since both statistics, $(\hat{p}_1 - \hat{p}_2)$ and $(\bar{y}_1 - \bar{y}_2)$, are approximately normally distributed, when n_1 and n_2 are large, we can use the inference-making techniques developed in chapters 6 and 7 for point estimation, interval estimation, and testing an hypothesis concerning the parameters, $(\mu_1 - \mu_2)$ and $(p_1 - p_2)$.

8.3 Estimation

To estimate θ, where θ is either $(\mu_1 - \mu_2)$ or $(p_1 - p_2)$, two random samples of size n_1 and n_2 are drawn and the estimate of θ is calculated using $\hat{\theta}$. As in section 6.2, the *point estimate* of θ is $\hat{\theta}$ with *bound on the error of estimation* given as $2\sigma_{\hat{\theta}}$.

Complete the following table, filling in the estimator and its standard deviation where required:

Parameter (θ)	Estimator ($\hat{\theta}$)	Standard Deviation ($\sigma_{\hat{\theta}}$)
$\mu_1 - \mu_2$	_____	_____ $\bar{y}_1 - \bar{y}_2$; $\sqrt{\dfrac{\sigma_1^2}{n_1} + \dfrac{\sigma_2^2}{n_2}}$
$p_1 - p_2$	$\hat{p}_1 - \hat{p}_2$	_____ $\sqrt{\dfrac{p_1 q_1}{n_1} + \dfrac{p_2 q_2}{n_2}}$

Notice that evaluation of the standard deviations given in the table may require values of parameters that are unknown. When the sample sizes are large, the sample estimates can be used to calculate an approximate standard deviation. As a rule of thumb, we will

1. Use _____ and _____ to approximate σ_1^2 and σ_2^2, respectively, as long as n_1 and n_2 are both larger than 30. $s_1^2; s_2^2$
2. Use _____ and _____ to approximate p_1 and p_2, respectively, as long as $n_1 p_1, n_1 q_1, n_2 p_2$, and $n_2 q_2$ are all greater than or equal to _____. $\hat{p}_1; \hat{p}_2$

10

For the following estimators, give the standard deviation and the best approximation of the standard deviation for use in confidence intervals.

Estimator ($\hat{\theta}$)	Standard Deviation ($\sigma_{\hat{\theta}}$)	Best Approximation of Standard Deviation ($\hat{\sigma}_{\hat{\theta}}$)	
$\bar{y}_1 - \bar{y}_2$	$\sqrt{\dfrac{\sigma_1^2}{n_1} + \dfrac{\sigma_2^2}{n_2}}$	$\sqrt{\rule{2cm}{0pt}}$	$\dfrac{s_1^2}{n_1} + \dfrac{s_2^2}{n_2}$
$\hat{p}_1 - \hat{p}_2$	$\sqrt{\rule{2cm}{0pt}}$	$\sqrt{\dfrac{\hat{p}_1 \hat{q}_1}{n_1} + \dfrac{\hat{p}_2 \hat{q}_2}{n_2}}$	$\dfrac{p_1 q_1}{n_1} + \dfrac{p_2 q_2}{n_2}$

Interval estimation is accomplished by constructing the confidence interval

$$\hat{\theta} \pm z\, \sigma_{\hat{\theta}}$$

where z values of 1.96, 1.645, or 2.58 correspond to 95%, 90%, or 99% confidence intervals, respectively.

Example 8.3

An experiment was conducted to compare the mean absorptions of drug in specimens of muscle tissue. Seventy-two tissue specimens were randomly divided between two drugs A and B with 36 assigned to each drug, and the drug absorption was measured for the 72 specimens. The means and variances for the two samples were $\bar{y}_1 = 7.8$, $s_1^2 = .10$ and $\bar{y}_2 = 8.4$, $s_2^2 = .06$, respectively. Find a 95% confidence interval for the difference in mean absorption rates.

Solution

We are interested in placing a confidence interval about the parameter

$(\mu_1 - \mu_2)$

_____. The confidence interval is approximately

$$(\bar{y}_1 - \bar{y}_2) \pm z \sqrt{\frac{s_1^2}{n_1} + \frac{s_2^2}{n_2}}$$

1.96

$$(7.8 - 8.4) \pm \underline{\quad\quad} \sqrt{\frac{.10}{36} + \frac{.06}{36}}$$

-.6

$$\underline{\quad\quad} \pm .131$$

-.731; -.469

or $\underline{\quad\quad} < \mu_1 - \mu_2 < \underline{\quad\quad}$

Example 8.4

The voting records at two precincts were compared based on samples of 400 voters from each precinct. Those voting Democratic numbered 209 and 263, respectively. Estimate the difference in the fraction voting Democratic for the two precincts, using a 90% confidence interval.

Solution

The confidence interval is approximately

$$(\hat{p}_1 - \hat{p}_2) \pm z \sqrt{\frac{\hat{p}_1 \hat{q}_1}{n_1} + \frac{\hat{p}_2 \hat{q}_2}{n_2}}$$

1.645

$$(.5225 - .6575) \pm \underline{\quad\quad} \sqrt{\frac{(.5225)(.4775)}{400} + \frac{(.6575)(.3425)}{400}}$$

-.135

$$\underline{\quad\quad} \pm .057$$

-.192; -.078

or $\underline{\quad\quad} < p_1 - p_2 < \underline{\quad\quad}$

Example 8.5

Refer to example 8.4. Place a bound on the error of estimation for $(\hat{p}_1 - \hat{p}_2)$, the estimate of $(p_1 - p_2)$.

Solution

-.135

The estimate of $(p_1 - p_2)$ is $\hat{p}_1 - \hat{p}_2 = \underline{\quad\quad}$ with the bound on error approximately equal to

$$2\sqrt{\frac{\hat{p}_1\hat{q}_1}{n_1}+\frac{\hat{p}_2\hat{q}_2}{n_2}}=2\sqrt{\underline{\hspace{2cm}}}$$

.0011867

$$=2(.0344)=\underline{\hspace{2cm}}$$

.069

Notice that the bound on error is (greater, less) than the half-width of the 90% confidence interval since it has reliability (_____) as compared to the confidence coefficient (_____) used for example 8.4.

greater
.95
.90

Self-Correcting Exercises 8A

1. In measuring the tensile strength of two alloys, strips of the alloys were subjected to tensile stress and the force (measured in pounds) at which the strip broke recorded for each strip. The data are summarized below.

	Alloy 1	Alloy 2
$\bar{y}$	150.5	160.2
s^2	23.72	36.37
n	35	35

Use these data to estimate the true mean difference in tensile strength by finding a point estimate for $(\mu_1-\mu_2)$ and placing a bound on the error of estimation.

2. Using the following data, give a point estimate with bounds on the error for the difference in mortality rates in breast cancers where radical or simple mastectomy was used as a treatment.

	Radical	Simple
Number died	31	41
Number treated	204	191

3. It is desired to estimate the difference in accident rates between youth and adult drivers. The following data were collected from two random samples, where y is the number of drivers that were involved in one or more accidents:

Youths	Adults
$n_1=100$	$n_2=200$
$y_1=50$	$y_2=60$

Estimate the difference (p_1-p_2) with a 95% confidence interval.

4. The yearly incomes of high school teachers in two cities yielded the following tabulation:

	City 1	City 2
Number of teachers	90	60
Average income	12,520	11,210
Standard deviation	1,510	950

a. If the teachers from each city are thought of as samples from two popula-tions of high school teachers, use the data to construct a 99% confidence interval for the difference in mean annual incomes.

b. Using the results of part a, would you be willing to conclude that these two city schools belong to populations having the same mean annual income?

8.4 A Large-Sample Test of an Hypothesis

As in chapter 7, we would like to test an hypothesis of the form

$$H_0: \quad \theta = \theta_0$$

against *one* of three alternative hypotheses:

(1) $H_a: \quad \theta \neq \underline{\qquad}$

(2) $H_a: \quad \theta > \theta_0$

or   (3) $H_a: \quad \theta \underline{\qquad}$

θ_0

$< \theta_0$

When the sample sizes are large, the estimator $\hat{\theta}$ is approximately normally dis-tributed and we can use

$$z = \frac{\hat{\theta} - \theta}{\sigma_{\hat{\theta}}}$$

as a test statistic, where θ is either $(\mu_1 - \mu_2)$ or $(p_1 - p_2)$ and $\hat{\theta}$ is either $(\bar{y}_1 - \bar{y}_2)$ or $(\hat{p}_1 - \hat{p}_2)$. In the comparison of two populations, the experimenter is often interested in determining whether or not there is a difference between the population parameters, μ_1 and μ_2 or p_1 and p_2. Hence, the discussion will be confined to a test of the null hypothesis

$$H_0: \quad \mu_1 = \mu_2 \quad \text{or, equivalently,} \quad H_0: \quad \mu_1 - \mu_2 = 0$$

and a test of the null hypothesis

$$H_0: \quad p_1 = p_2 \quad \text{or, equivalently,} \quad H_0: \quad p_1 - p_2 = 0$$

Test of an Hypothesis Concerning $(\mu_1 - \mu_2)$

In order to test the null hypothesis $H_0: \mu_1 - \mu_2 = 0$ against either a one- or a two-tailed alternative hypothesis of the form

(1) $H_a: \mu_1 - \mu_2 \neq 0$

(2) $H_a: \mu_1 - \mu_2 > 0$

or (3) $H_a: \mu_1 - \mu_2 < 0$

the test statistic is

$$z = \frac{\bar{y}_1 - \bar{y}_2 - (\mu_1 - \mu_2)}{\sqrt{\dfrac{\sigma_1^2}{n_1} + \dfrac{\sigma_2^2}{n_2}}}$$

The test statistic z is calculated assuming that H_0 is true and thus $(\mu_1 - \mu_2)$ is set equal to _____. The values for σ_1^2 and σ_2^2 are unknown but can be estimated by s_1^2 and s_2^2 as long as n_1 and n_2 are larger than 30.   zero

The rejection region for this test is based on the standard normal distribution; and, for a given value of α, the decision is made based on the calculated value of the test statistic.

Example 8.6

Suppose an educator is interested in testing whether a new teaching technique is superior to an old teaching technique. The criterion will be a test given at the end of a 6-week period and the technique resulting in a significantly higher score will be judged superior. Based on the following sample data, test the hypothesis that the test means for the techniques are the same against the alternative hypothesis that the new technique is superior at the $\alpha = .05$ level.

	New Technique	Old Technique
	$\bar{y}_1 = 69.2$	$\bar{y}_2 = 67.5$
	$s_1^2 = 49.3$	$s_2^2 = 64.5$
	$n_1 = 50$	$n_2 = 80$

Solution

1. $H_0: \mu_1 - \mu_2 =$ _____   0

2. $H_a: \mu_1 - \mu_2 > 0$

3. Test statistic:

$$z = \frac{(\bar{y}_1 - \bar{y}_2) - 0}{\sqrt{\dfrac{s_1^2}{n_1} + \dfrac{s_2^2}{n_2}}}$$

(since σ_1^2 and σ_2^2 are unknown).

4. Rejection region:

1.645

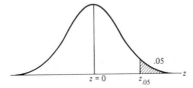

$z = 0$ $z_{.05}$

Reject H_0 if $z >$ _____ .

Computing the value of the test statistic,

69.2; 67.5

$$z = \frac{(\underline{\quad\quad} - \underline{\quad\quad}) - 0}{\sqrt{\dfrac{49.3}{50} + \dfrac{64.5}{80}}}$$

1.7; 1.27

$$= \frac{\underline{\quad\quad}}{\sqrt{716.9/400}} = \frac{1.7}{1.34} = \underline{\quad\quad}$$

does not; will not

Since the value of z (does, does not) fall in the rejection region, we (will, will not) reject H_0. Before deciding to accept H_0 as true, we may wish to evaluate the probability of a type II error for meaningful values of $(\mu_1 - \mu_2)$ described by H_a. Until this is done, we will state our decision as "do not reject H_0."

Test of an Hypothesis Concerning $(p_1 - p_2)$
In order to test the null hypothesis $H_0 : p_1 - p_2 = 0$ against either a one- or two-tailed alternative of the form

(1) $H_a : p_1 - p_2 \neq 0$

(2) $H_a : p_1 - p_2 > 0$

or   (3) $H_a : p_1 - p_2 < 0$

the test statistic is

$$z = \frac{(\hat{p}_1 - \hat{p}_2) - (p_1 - p_2)}{\sqrt{\hat{p}\hat{q}\left(\dfrac{1}{n_1} + \dfrac{1}{n_2}\right)}} \qquad \text{where} \qquad \hat{p} = \frac{y_1 + y_2}{n_1 + n_2}$$

The test statistic z is calculated assuming that H_0 is true and thus $(p_1 - p_2)$ is set
equal to _____. Since p_1 and p_2 are assumed equal to the same common   zero
value, p, it seems reasonable to use the same sample estimate for both p_1 and p_2.
This common estimate is a "pooled" sample percentage of successes, given as

$$\hat{p} = \frac{\text{total number of successes}}{\text{total number of trials}} = \frac{y_1 + y_2}{n_1 + n_2}$$

The rejection region for this test is again based on a standard normal distribution, with a decision being made based on the calculated value of the test
statistic.

Example 8.7

To investigate possible differences in attitude about a current political problem,
100 randomly selected voters between the ages of 18 and 25 were polled and
100 randomly selected voters over age 25 were polled. Each was asked if he or
she agreed with the government's position on the problem. Forty-five of the first
group agreed, while 63% of the second group agreed. Do these data represent a
significant difference in attitude for these two groups?

Solution

This problem involves a test of the difference between two binomial proportions, $(p_1 - p_2)$. The relevant data are given in the table.

	Group 1	Group 2
n	100	100
$\hat{p}$	.45	.63

1. H_0: $p_1 - p_2$ _____   = 0

2. H_a: $p_1 - p_2$ _____   ≠ 0

3. For testing the hypothesis of *no difference* between proportions, the test statistic is

$$z = \frac{(\hat{p}_1 - \hat{p}_2) - 0}{\sqrt{\hat{p}\hat{q}\left(\frac{1}{n_1} + \frac{1}{n_2}\right)}}$$

with

$$\hat{p} = \frac{y_1 + y_2}{n_1 + n_2}$$

4. Rejection region:

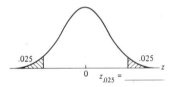

1.96

1.96

.54

−.18

−2.55

reject
is

For a two-tailed test with $\alpha = .05$, we will reject H_0 if $|z| >$ _____.
To calculate the test statistic, we need

$$\hat{p} = \frac{y_1 + y_2}{n_1 + n_2} = \frac{45 + 63}{200} = \text{_____}$$

Then

$$z = \frac{(.45 - .63) - 0}{\sqrt{(.54)(.46)(2/100)}}$$

$$= \text{_____} / .0705$$

$$= \text{_____}$$

Since $|-2.55| = 2.55 > 1.96$, we (reject, do not reject) H_0 and conclude that there (is, is not) a significant difference in opinion between these two age groups with respect to this issue.

Self-Correcting Exercises 8B

1. To investigate a possible "built-in" sex bias in a graduate school entrance examination, 50 male and 50 female graduate students who were rated as above-average graduate students by their professors were selected to participate in the study by actually taking this test. Their test results on this examination are summarized in the following table.

	Males	Females
$\bar{y}$	720	693
s^2	104	85
n	50	50

   Do these data indicate that males will, on the average, score higher than females of the same ability on this exam? (Use $\alpha = .05$.)
2. Give the level of significance for the test performed in exercise 1. Based on this p value, what would your decision be?

3. Random samples of 100 shoes manufactured by machine A and 50 shoes manufactured by machine B showed 16 and 6 defective shoes, respectively. Do these data present sufficient evidence to suggest a difference in the performances of the machines? (Use $\alpha = .05$.)

EXERCISES

1. List the two essential elements of any inference-making procedure.
2. An appliance dealer sells toasters of two different brands, brand A and brand B. Let p_1 denote the fraction of brand A toasters that are returned to him by customers as defective, and let p_2 represent the fraction of brand B toasters that are rejected by customers as defective. Suppose that of 200 brand A toasters sold, 14 were returned as defective, while of 450 brand B toasters sold, 18 were returned as defective. Provide a 90% confidence interval for $(p_1 - p_2)$.
3. To compare the effect of stress in the form of noise upon the ability to perform a simple task, 70 subjects were divided into two groups: the first group of 30 subjects was to act as a control while the second group of 40 was to be the experimental group. Although each subject performed the task in the same control room, each of the experimental-group subjects had to perform the task while loud rock music was being played in the room. The time to finish the task was recorded for each subject and the following summary was obtained:

	Control	Experimental
n	30	40
$\bar{y}$	15 minutes	23 minutes
s	4 minutes	10 minutes

   Find a 99% confidence interval for the difference in mean completion times for these two groups.
4. Refer to exercise 3. Does it appear that stress in the form of noise is in fact increasing the completion time? Give the level of significance for the appropriate test of hypothesis and make a decision based upon this value.
5. To test the effectiveness of a vaccine, 150 experimental animals were given the vaccine and 150 were not. All 300 were then infected with the disease. Among those vaccinated, 10 died as a result of the disease. In the control group (i.e., those not vaccinated), there were 30 deaths. Can we conclude that the vaccine is effective in reducing the mortality rate? (Use a significance level of .01.)
6. Two diets were to be compared. Seventy-five individuals were selected at random from a population of overweight people. Forty of this group were assigned diet A and the other 35 were placed on diet B. The weight losses in

pounds over a period of 1 week were found and the following quantities recorded:

	Sample Size	Sample Mean (pounds)	Sample Variance
Diet A	40	10.3	7
Diet B	35	7.3	3.25

a. Do these data allow the conclusion that the expected weight loss under diet A (μ_A) is greater than the expected weight loss under diet B (μ_B)? Test at the .01 level. Draw the appropriate conclusion.
b. Construct a 90% confidence interval for ($\mu_A - \mu_B$).

7. Last year's records of auto accidents occurring on a given section of highway were classified according to whether the resulting damage was $200 or more and to whether or not a physical injury resulted from the accident. The tabulation follows:

	Under $200	$200 or more
Number of accidents	32	41
Number involving injuries	10	23

a. Estimate the true proportion of accidents involving injuries and damage of $200 or more for similar sections of highway and place bounds on the error of estimation.
b. Estimate the true difference in proportion of accidents involving injuries for accidents involving less than $200 in damage and those involving $200 or more with a 95% confidence interval.

Chapter 9

INFERENCES BASED ON SMALL SAMPLES

9.1 Introduction

Large-sample methods for making inferences about a population were considered in chapters 6, 7, and 8. When the sample size was large, the _____ Theorem assured the approximate normality of the distribution of the estimators $\bar{y}$ or $\hat{p}$. However, time, cost, or other limitations may prevent an investigator from collecting enough data to feel confident in using large-sample techniques. When the sample size is small, $n < 30$, the Central Limit Theorem may no longer apply. This difficulty can be overcome if the investigator is reasonably sure that his or her measurements constitute a sample from a _____ population.

    The results presented in this chapter are based on the assumption that the observations being analyzed have been _____ drawn from a *normal* population. This assumption is not as restrictive as it sounds, since the normal distribution can be used as a model in cases where the underlying distribution is mound-shaped and fairly symmetrical.

Central
Limit

normal

randomly

9.2 Student's *t* Distribution

When the sample size is large, the statistic

$$\frac{\bar{y} - \mu}{\sigma/\sqrt{n}}$$

is approximately distributed as the standard normal random variable z. What can be said about this statistic when n, the sample size, is small and the sample variance s^2 is used to estimate σ^2?

If the parent population is not normal (nor approximately normal), the behavior of the statistic given above is not known in general when n is small. Its distribution could be empirically generated by repeated sampling from the population of interest. If the parent population *is* normal, we can rely upon the results of W. S. Gosset, who published under the pen name Student. He drew repeated samples from a normal population and tabulated the distribution of a statistic which he called t, where

$$t = \frac{\bar{y} - \mu}{s/\sqrt{n}}$$

The resulting distribution for t has the following properties:

$t = 0$

mound
symmetrical
more

n

standard normal

normal
mound

random

one; $\bar{y}$

1. The distribution is _____-shaped.
2. The distribution is _____ about the value $t = 0$.
3. The distribution has more flaring tails than z; hence t is (more, less) variable than the z statistic.
4. The shape of the distribution changes as the value of _____ , the sample size, changes.
5. As the sample size n becomes large, the t distribution becomes identical to the _____ _____ distribution.

These results are based on the following two assumptions:

1. The parent population has a _____ distribution. The t statistic is, however, relatively stable for nonnormal _____-shaped distributions.
2. The sample is a _____ sample. When the population is normal, this assures us that $\bar{y}$ and s^2 are independent.

For a fixed sample size, n, the statistic

$$z = \frac{\bar{y} - \mu}{\sigma/\sqrt{n}}$$

contains exactly _____ random quantity, the sample mean _____ . However, the statistic

$$t = \frac{\bar{y} - \mu}{s/\sqrt{n}}$$

contains exactly _____ random quantities, _____ and _____. This accounts for the fact that *t* is (more, less) variable than *z*.   two; $\bar{y}$

s; more

In fact, $\bar{y}$ may be large while *s* is small or $\bar{y}$ may be small while *s* is large. Hence it is said that $\bar{y}$ and *s* are _____, which means that the value assumed by $\bar{y}$ in no way determines the value of *s*.   independent

As the sample size changes, the corresponding *t* distribution changes so that each value of *n* determines a different probability distribution. This is due to the variability of s^2, which appears in the denominator of *t*. Large sample sizes produce (more, less) stable estimates of σ^2 than do small sample sizes. These different probability curves are identified by the *degrees of freedom* associated with the estimator of σ^2, a quantity which is directly related to the sample size. For the test statistic,   more

$$t = \frac{\bar{y} - \mu}{s/\sqrt{n}}$$

the degrees of freedom will always be _____, where *n* is the sample size,   *n* – 1

and the resulting *t* distribution is indexed as having _____ degrees of   *n* – 1

freedom.

The Use of Tables for the t Distribution

We define t_a as that value of *t* having an area equal to *a* to its _____,   right

and $-t_a$ is that value of *t* having an area equal to *a* to its _____.   left

Consider the following diagram:

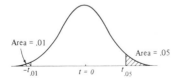

The distribution of *t* is _____ about the value *t* = 0; hence, only the   symmetrical

positive values of *t* need be tabulated. Problems involving left-tailed values of *t* can be solved in terms of right-tailed values, as was done with the *z* statistic. A negative value of *t* simply indicates that you are working in the (left, right) tail   left

of the distribution.

Table 2 of the text tabulates *commonly used* critical values, t_a, based on 1, 2, ..., 29, ∞ degrees of freedom for *a* = .100, .050, .025, .010, .005. Along the top margin of the table you will find columns labeled t_a for the various values of *a*, while along the right margin you will find a column marked degrees of freedom, d.f. By cross-indexing you can find the value *t* having an area equal to *a* to its right and having the proper degrees of freedom.

Example 9.1

To find the critical value of *t* for *a* = .05 with 5 degrees of freedom, find 5 in the

2.179

30

σ

2.920
3.169
1.313
2.583
2.086

t

$z; z$

right margin. Now by reading across, you will find $t = 2.015$ in the $t_{.05}$ column. In the same manner, we find that for 12 degrees of freedom, $t_{.025} = $ _____. In using Table 2, think of your problem in terms of a, the area to the right of the value of t, and the degrees of freedom.

Compare the different values of t based on an infinite number of degrees of freedom with those for a corresponding z. You can perhaps see the reason for choosing a sample size greater than _____ as the dividing point for using the z distribution when the standard deviation s is used as an estimate for

_____.

Example 9.2

Find the critical values for t when t_a is that value of t with an area of a to its right, based on the following degrees of freedom:

	a	d.f.	t
a.	.05	2	_____
b.	.005	10	_____
c.	.10	28	_____
d.	.01	16	_____
e.	.025	20	_____

Students taking their first course in statistics usually ask the following questions at this point: "How will I know whether I should use z or t? Is sample size the only criterion I should apply?" No, sample size is not the only criterion to be used. When the sample size is *large*, both

$$T_1 = \frac{\bar{y} - \mu}{\sigma/\sqrt{n}} \quad \text{and} \quad T_2 = \frac{\bar{y} - \mu}{s/\sqrt{n}}$$

behave as a standard normal random variable z, regardless of the distribution of the parent population. When the sample size is *small* and the sampled population is *not normal*, then, in general, neither T_1 nor T_2 behaves as z or t. In the special case when the parent population is *normal*, then T_1 behaves as z and T_2 behaves as t.

Use this information to complete the following table when the sample is drawn from a *normal* distribution:

Statistic	Sample Size	
	$n < 30$	$n \geqslant 30$
$\dfrac{\bar{y} - \mu}{s/\sqrt{n}}$	_____	t or app. z
$\dfrac{\bar{y} - \mu}{\sigma/\sqrt{n}}$	_____	_____

9.3 Small-Sample Inferences Concerning a Population Mean

Small-Sample Test Concerning a Population Mean μ
A test of an hypothesis concerning the mean μ of a *normal* population when $n < 30$ and σ is unknown proceeds as follows:

1. $H_0: \mu = \mu_0$

2. H_a: appropriate one- or two-tailed alternative

3. Test statistic:

$$t = \frac{\bar{y} - \mu}{s/\sqrt{n}}$$

4. Rejection region with $\alpha = P(\text{falsely rejecting } H_0)$:
   a. For $H_a: \mu > \mu_0$, reject H_0 if $t > t_\alpha$ based on $n - 1$ degrees of freedom.
   b. For $H_a: \mu < \mu_0$, reject H_0 if $t < -t_\alpha$ based on $n - 1$ degrees of freedom.
   c. For $H_a: \mu \neq \mu_0$, reject H_0 if $|t| > t_{\alpha/2}$ based on $n - 1$ degrees of freedom.

Example 9.3
A new electronic device that requires 2 hours per item to produce on a production line has been developed by company *A*. While the new product is being run, profitable production time is used. Hence the manufacturer decides to produce only six new items for testing purposes. For each of the six items, the time to failure is measured, yielding the measurements 59.2, 68.3, 57.8, 56.5, 63.7, and 57.3 hours. Is there sufficient evidence to indicate that the new device has a mean life greater than 55 hours at the $\alpha = .05$ level?

Solution
To calculate the sample mean and standard deviation we need

$$\Sigma y = 362.8 \quad \text{and} \quad \Sigma y^2 = 22{,}043.60$$

$$\bar{y} = \frac{\Sigma y}{n} = \frac{362.8}{6} = \underline{\hspace{2cm}}$$

60.47

$$s^2 = \frac{1}{n-1}\left[\Sigma y^2 - \frac{(\Sigma y)^2}{n}\right]$$

$$= \frac{1}{5}\left[22{,}043.60 - \frac{(362.8)^2}{6}\right]$$

$$= \underline{\hspace{2cm}}$$

21.2587

4.61

with $s = \sqrt{21.2587} =$ _____

The test proceeds as follows:

= 55

1. $H_0: \mu$ _____

> 55

2. $H_a: \mu$ _____

3. Test statistic:

$$t = \frac{\bar{y} - 55}{s/\sqrt{n}}$$

4. Rejection region:

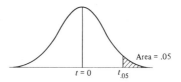

Area = .05

$t = 0$ $t_{.05}$

2.015

Based on 5 degrees of freedom, reject H_0 if $t >$ _____ . Now calculate the value of the test statistic:

60.47; 5.47; 2.91
4.61

$$t = \frac{\bar{y} - 55}{s/\sqrt{n}} = \frac{\text{_____} - 55}{\text{_____}/\sqrt{6}} = \frac{\text{_____}}{1.88} = \text{_____}$$

is; reject
is

Since the observed value (is, is not) larger than 2.015, we (reject, do not reject) H_0. There (is, is not) sufficient evidence to indicate that the new device has a mean life greater than 55 hours at the 5% level of significance.

Confidence Interval for a Population Mean μ

In estimating a population mean, we can use either a point estimator with bounds on the error of estimation or an interval estimator having the required level of confidence.

    Small sample estimation of the mean of a *normal* population with σ *unknown* involves the statistic

$$\frac{\bar{y} - \mu}{s/\sqrt{n}}$$

$t; n - 1$

which has a _____ distribution with _____ degrees of freedom. The resulting confidence interval estimator is given as

$$\bar{y} \pm t \frac{s}{\sqrt{n}}$$

The value of t corresponding to a 90%, 95%, or 99% confidence interval is found in Table 2 of the text by indexing $n - 1$ degrees of freedom and $a = .05, .025,$ or .005. The lower confidence limit is _____ and the upper confidence limit is _____ . The point estimator of μ is _____ and the bound on the error of estimation can be taken to be $ts/\sqrt{n}$. A proper interpretation of a 95% confidence interval for μ would be stated as follows: In repeated sampling, _____ of the _____ _____ so constructed would enclose the true value of the mean μ.

$\bar{y} - ts/\sqrt{n}$
$\bar{y} + ts/\sqrt{n}; \bar{y}$

95%; confidence intervals

Example 9.4
Using the data from example 9.3 of this section, find a 95% confidence interval estimate for μ, the mean life in hours for the new device.

Solution
The pertinent information from example 9.3 follows.

$\bar{y} = 60.47$ d.f. = _____   5

$s/\sqrt{n} = 1.88$ $t_{.025} =$ _____   2.571

The confidence interval will be found by using

$$\bar{y} \pm t_{.025} s/\sqrt{n}$$

Substituting $\bar{y}$, $s/\sqrt{n}$, and $t_{.025}$, we have

60.47 ± _____ (1.88)   2.571

60.47 ± _____   4.83

or   (_____ , _____)   55.64; 65.30

Self-Correcting Exercises 9A

1. In a random sample of ten cans of corn from supplier B, the average weight per can of corn was $\bar{y} = 9.4$ ounces, with a standard deviation of $s = 1.8$ ounces. Does this sample contain sufficient evidence to indicate that the mean weight is less than 10 ounces at the $\alpha = .01$ level? Find a 99% confidence interval for μ.
2. A school administrator claimed that the average time spent on a school bus by those students in his school district that rode school buses was 35 min-

utes. A random sample of 20 students who did ride the school buses yielded an average of 42 minutes riding time with a standard deviation of 6.2 minutes. Does this sample of size 20 contain sufficient evidence to indicate that the mean riding time is greater than 35 minutes at the 5% level of significance?

3. Find a 95% confidence interval for the mean time spent on a school bus, using the data from exercise 2.

9.4 Small-Sample Inferences Concerning the Difference Between Two Means $(\mu_1 - \mu_2)$

Inferences concerning $(\mu_1 - \mu_2)$ based on small samples are founded upon the following assumptions:

normal

1. Each population sampled has a _____ distribution.

variances

2. The population _____ are equal; that is, $\sigma_1^2 = \sigma_2^2$.
3. The samples are independently drawn.

$\bar{y}_1 - \bar{y}_2$

A good estimator for $(\mu_1 - \mu_2)$, regardless of sample size, is _____.
The standard deviation of this estimator is

$$\sqrt{\frac{\sigma_1^2}{n_1} + \frac{\sigma_2^2}{n_2}}$$

When $\sigma_1^2 = \sigma_2^2$, we can replace σ_1^2 and σ_2^2 by a common variance σ^2. Then the standard deviation of $(\bar{y}_1 - \bar{y}_2)$ becomes

σ

$$\sqrt{\frac{\sigma^2}{n_1} + \frac{\sigma^2}{n_2}} = (\underline{\hspace{1.5cm}}) \sqrt{\frac{1}{n_1} + \frac{1}{n_2}}$$

If σ were known, then in testing an hypothesis concerning $(\mu_1 - \mu_2)$, we would use the statistic

$$z = \frac{(\bar{y}_1 - \bar{y}_2) - D_0}{\sigma \sqrt{\frac{1}{n_1} + \frac{1}{n_2}}}$$

where $D_0 = \mu_1 - \mu_2$. For small samples with σ unknown, we would use

$$t = \frac{(\bar{y}_1 - \bar{y}_2) - D_0}{s \sqrt{\frac{1}{n_1} + \frac{1}{n_2}}}$$

where s is the estimate of σ, calculated from the sample values. When the data

are normally distributed, this statistic has a _____ _____ distri-   Student's t
bution with degrees of freedom, $(n_1 + n_2 - 2)$.

In selecting the best estimate (s^2) for σ^2, we have three immediate choices:

a. s_1^2, the sample variance from population _____   I

b. s_2^2, the sample variance from population _____   II

c. A combination of _____ and _____ $s_1^2 ; s_2^2$

The best choice is $(a, b, c,)$, since it uses the information from both samples. A   c
logical method of combining this information into one estimate, s^2, is

d.
$$s^2 = \frac{(n_1 - 1)s_1^2 + (n_2 - 1)s_2^2}{(n_1 - 1) + (n_2 - 1)}$$

a weighted average of the sample variances using the degrees of freedom as
weights.

The expression in d can be written in another form by replacing s_1^2 and s_2^2 by
their defining formulas. Then

$$s^2 = \frac{\Sigma(y - \bar{y}_1)^2 + \Sigma(y - \bar{y}_2)^2}{(n_1 - 1) + (n_2 - 1)}$$

In this form we see that we have pooled or added the sums of squared deviations
from each sample and divided by the pooled degrees of freedom, $(n_1 + n_2 - 2)$.
Hence s^2 is a *pooled estimate* of the common variance σ^2 and is based on
_____ degrees of freedom. Since our samples were drawn from nor- $n_1 + n_2 - 2$
mal populations, the statistic

$$t = \frac{(\bar{y}_1 - \bar{y}_2) - (\mu_1 - \mu_2)}{s\sqrt{\dfrac{1}{n_1} + \dfrac{1}{n_2}}}$$

has a _____ _____ distribution with _____ degrees   Student's t; $n_1 + n_2 - 2$
of freedom.

Example 9.5
A medical student conducted a diet study using two groups of 12 rats each as
subjects. Group I received diet I while group II received diet II. After 5 weeks
the student calculated the gain in weight for each rat. The data yielded the following information:

Group I	Group II
$\bar{y}_1 = 6.8$ ounces	$\bar{y}_2 = 5.3$ ounces
$s_1 = 1.5$ ounces	$s_2 = .9$ ounce
$n_1 = 12$	$n_2 = 12$

Do these data present sufficient evidence to indicate, at the $\alpha = .05$ level, that rats on diet I will gain more weight than those on diet II?

Solution

We will take the gains in weight to be normally distributed with equal variances and calculate a pooled estimate for σ^2.

$$s^2 = \frac{(n_1 - 1)s_1^2 + (n_2 - 1)s_2^2}{n_1 + n_2 - 2}$$

1.530

$$= \frac{11(1.5)^2 + 11(.9)^2}{12 + 12 - 2} = \frac{33.66}{22} = \underline{\hspace{1.5cm}}$$

so that

1.237

$$s = \sqrt{1.530} = \underline{\hspace{1.5cm}}$$

The test is as follows.

0

1. H_0: $\mu_1 - \mu_2 = \underline{\hspace{1.5cm}}$

0

2. H_a: $\mu_1 - \mu_2 > \underline{\hspace{1.5cm}}$

3. Test statistic:

$$t = \frac{(\bar{y}_1 - \bar{y}_2) - D_0}{s\sqrt{\dfrac{1}{n_1} + \dfrac{1}{n_2}}}$$

4. Rejection region:

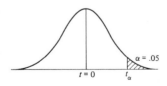

$\alpha = .05$

$t = 0$ t_α

22
1.717

With $n_1 + n_2 - 2 = \underline{\hspace{1.5cm}}$ degrees of freedom, we would reject H_0 if $t > \underline{\hspace{1.5cm}}$. Now we calculate the value of the test statistic.

$$t = \frac{(\bar{y}_1 - \bar{y}_2) - D_0}{s \sqrt{\dfrac{1}{n_1} + \dfrac{1}{n_2}}}$$

$$= \frac{(\underline{\hspace{1.5cm}}) - (\underline{\hspace{1.5cm}})}{1.237 \sqrt{.1667}}$$

1.5; 0

$$= \frac{(\underline{\hspace{1.5cm}})}{.505}$$

1.5

$$= \underline{\hspace{1.5cm}}$$

2.97

Decision: _____ .

Reject H_0

A *small-sample confidence interval for* $(\mu_1 - \mu_2)$ is given as

$$(\bar{y}_1 - \bar{y}_2) \pm ts \sqrt{\frac{1}{n_1} + \frac{1}{n_2}}$$

where

$$s = \sqrt{\frac{(n_1 - 1)s_1^2 + (n_2 - 1)s_2^2}{n_1 + n_2 - 2}}$$

and the t value for a 90%, 95%, or 99% confidence interval is found in Table 2 of the text by indexing d.f. $= n_1 + n_2 - 2$ and $a = .05, .025,$ or $.005$, respectively.

Example 9.6
Refer to example 9.5. Find a 90% confidence interval for $(\mu_1 - \mu_2)$.

Solution
To find a 90% confidence interval for $(\mu_1 - \mu_2)$, we need $t_{.05}$ based on 22 degrees of freedom. $t_{.05} = \underline{\hspace{1.5cm}}$. Hence we would use

1.717

$$(\bar{y}_1 - \bar{y}_2) \pm 1.717s \sqrt{\frac{1}{n_1} + \frac{1}{n_2}}$$

$$\underline{\hspace{2cm}} \pm 1.717 (\underline{\hspace{2cm}})$$

1.5; .505

$$(\underline{\hspace{1.5cm}}) \pm (\underline{\hspace{1.5cm}})$$

1.5; .867

Therefore, a 90% confidence interval for $(\mu_1 - \mu_2)$ would be

.63; 2.37

(_____, _____).

Self-Correcting Exercises 9B

1. What are the assumptions required for the proper use of the statistic

$$t = \frac{(\bar{y}_1 - \bar{y}_2) - (\mu_1 - \mu_2)}{s \sqrt{\dfrac{1}{n_1} + \dfrac{1}{n_2}}}$$

2. In the process of making a decision to either continue operating or close a civic health center, a random sample of 25 people who had visited the center at least once was chosen and each person asked whether he or she felt the center should be closed. In addition, the distance between each person's place of residence and the health center was computed and recorded. Of the 25 people responding, 16 were in favor of continued operation. For these 16 people, the average distance from the center was 5.2 miles with a standard deviation of 2.8 miles. The remaining 9 people who were in favor of closing the center lived at an average of 8.7 miles from the center with a standard deviation of 5.3 miles. Do these data indicate that there is a significant difference in mean distance to the health center for these two groups?

3. Estimate the difference in mean distance to the health center for the two groups in exercise 2 with a 95% confidence interval.

4. In investigating which of two presentations of subject matter to use in a computer-programmed course, an experimenter randomly chose two groups of 18 students each, and assigned one group to receive presentation I and the second to receive presentation II. A short quiz on the presentation was given to each group and their grades recorded. Do the following data indicate that a difference in the mean quiz scores (hence a difference in effectiveness of presentation) exists for the two methods?

	$\bar{y}$	s^2
Presentation I	81.7	23.2
Presentation II	77.2	19.8

9.5 Summary

The testing and estimation procedures presented in this chapter are based on the t distribution. In order that the probability statements associated with these testing and estimation procedures accurately reflect the prescribed probability values, specific assumptions concerning the sampled population(s) and the method of sampling must be satisfied.

The valid use of the t statistic requires that all samples be randomly selected from _____ populations. When two samples are drawn, the samples must be drawn _____. In addition, when making inferences about the difference in two population means μ_1 and μ_2 using two independent samples, the population variances σ_1^2 and σ_2^2 must be _____.

normal
independently

equal

It would be unusual to have all these assumptions satisfied in practice. However, if the sampled population were not normal, or $\sigma_1^2 \neq \sigma_2^2$, we would like our procedures to produce error probabilities that are approximately equal to the specified values. A statistical procedure that is insensitive to departures from the assumptions upon which it is based is said to be _____.

robust

Procedures based on the t statistic are fairly robust to departures from normality provided that the sampled population(s) is(are) not strongly skewed. The t statistic used in comparing two means is moderately robust to departures from the assumption $\sigma_1^2 = \sigma_2^2$ when $n_1 = n_2$. However, when $\sigma_1^2 \neq \sigma_2^2$ and one sample size becomes large relative to the other, the procedure fails to be robust.

When an experimenter is aware of possible violations of assumptions, the usual procedure can be used if it is robust with respect to the assumptions violated. Otherwise, the nonparametric procedures presented in chapter 15 can be used. Nonparametric methods require few or no assumptions concerning the sampled population(s); however, samples must nonetheless be _____ selected, and when appropriate, the samples must also be independently drawn. When the sample sizes are relatively large, techniques such as those presented in chapters 6, 7, and 8 can be used in place of nonparametric procedures.

randomly

EXERCISES

1. Why can we say that the test statistics employed in chapters 6, 7, and 8 are approximately normally distributed?

2. What assumptions are made when Student's t statistic is used to test an hypothesis concerning a population mean μ?

3. How does one determine the degrees of freedom associated with a t statistic?

4. Ten butterfat determinations for brand G milk were carried out yielding $\bar{y} = 3.7\%$ and $s = 1.7\%$. Do these results produce sufficient evidence to indicate that brand G milk contains, on the average, less than 4.0% butterfat? (Use $\alpha = .05$.)

5. Refer to exercise 4. Estimate the mean percentage of butterfat for brand G milk with a 95% confidence interval.

6. An experimenter has developed a new fertilizing technique that should increase the production of cabbages. Do the following data produce sufficient evidence to indicate that the mean weight of those cabbages grown by using the new technique is greater than the mean weight of those grown by using the standard technique?

	Population I (New Technique)	Population II (Standard Technique)
	$n_1 = 16$	$n_2 = 10$
	$\bar{y}_1 = 33.4$ ounces	$\bar{y}_2 = 31.8$ ounces
	$s_1 = 3$ ounces	$s_2 = 4$ ounces

7. Find a 90% confidence interval for the difference in means $(\mu_1 - \mu_2)$ for the data given in exercise 6.

8. A manufacturer of electronic calculators has specified in its marketing ads that Model 23X will draw no more than .4 amperes of current under normal operating conditions. Fifteen Model 23X calculators were tested, and it was found that the average current drawn was .44 amperes with a standard deviation of .09 amperes. Does this sample contain sufficient evidence to refute the manufacturer's claim at the .05 level of significance?

9. Prior to deciding whether to use a riveting procedure or a spot welding procedure in manufacturing a new product, a research and development team decided to test the shear strength of metal bonded using these two procedures. Tests for shear strength on 10 items bonded using the riveting procedure and 10 items bonded using the spot welding procedure produced the following data summary on shear strength measured in pounds.

	Rivets	Spot Weld
$\bar{y}$	550 lbs.	510 lbs.
s^2	710	1018
n	10	10

Do these data indicate that there is a significant difference in mean shear strength for these two procedures at the .05 level of significance?

10. Estimate the difference in mean shear strength for the two procedures in exercise 9 with a 90% confidence interval.

11. In an experiment to assess the effect of hormone imbalance on food intake in rats, 8 randomly selected animals were administered doses of a specific hormone in their drinking water, and the amount of food consumed in grams was recorded for each rat. At the termination of the experiment the rats had consumed 58.6, 68.1, 55.2, 64.1, 59.6, 57.2, 57.5, and 61.3 grams of food. Does this sample contain sufficient evidence to indicate that the average food intake for this group is significantly greater than 60 grams, the average during a similar period for rats not administered the hormone? (Use $\alpha = .01$.)

Chapter   10
REGRESSION AND CORRELATION

10.1   Introduction

We have investigated the problem of making inferences about population parameters in the case of large and small sample sizes. We will now consider another
aspect of this problem. Suppose that the value of a random variable y depends to
some extent upon the values assigned to other variables $x_1, x_2, x_3, \ldots, x_k$.
Since the values of y depend to some extent on the values assumed by $x_1, x_2,$
$\ldots, x_k$, y is called the *dependent variable* and $x_1, x_2, \ldots, x_k$ are called the *independent variables*. It will be our objective to try to predict the value assumed
by y through knowledge of $x_1, x_2, \ldots, x_k$. A mathematical equation will be
used as the prediction equation, expressing y as a function of the independent
variables $x_1, x_2, \ldots, x_k$.

We will first consider the problem of relating y to a single independent variable x. The multivariable problem will be discussed, with solutions available
through the use of a computer. We restrict our investigation to the case where
the average value of y is a *linear* function of x. That is, the relationship between
the average value of y and x can be described by a straight line.

Review: The Algebraic Representation of a Straight Line

To understand the development of the following linear models, you must be
familiar with the algebraic representation of a straight line and its properties.

The mathematical equation for a straight line is

$$y = \beta_0 + \beta_1 x$$

where x is the independent variable, y is the dependent variable, and β_0 and β_1
are fixed constants. When values of x are substituted into this equation, pairs of
numbers, (x, y), are generated which, when plotted or graphed on a rectangular
coordinate system, form a straight line.

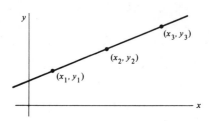

Consider the graph of a linear equation $y = \beta_0 + \beta_1 x$, shown below.

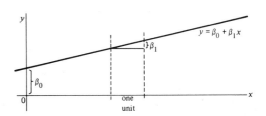

intercept

slope

1. By setting $x = 0$, we have $y = \beta_0 + \beta_1(0) = \beta_0$. Because the line intercepts or cuts the y-axis at the value $y = \beta_0$, β_0 is called the y _____.
2. The constant β_1 represents the increase in y for a one-unit increase in x and is called the _____ of the line.

Example 10.1
Plot the equation $y = 1 + .5x$ on a rectangular coordinate system.

Solution
Two points are needed to uniquely determine a straight line and therefore a minimum of two points must be found. A third point is usually found as a check on calculations.
1. Using 0, 2, and 4 as values of x, find the corresponding values of y.

1
2
3

   a. When $x = 0, y = 1 + .5(0) =$ _____.
   b. When $x = 2, y = 1 + .5(2) =$ _____.
   c. When $x = 4, y = 1 + .5(4) =$ _____.
2. Plot these points on a rectangular coordinate system and join them by using a straightedge.

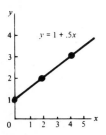

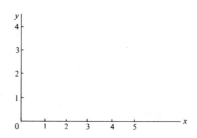

Practice plotting the following linear equations on a rectangular coordinate system:

a. $y = -1 + 3x.$ d. $y = x.$

b. $y = 2 - x.$ e. $y = .5 + 2x.$

c. $y = -.5 - .5x.$

10.2 Scatter Diagrams and the Freehand Regression Line

1. Suppose we are given a set consisting of n pairs of values for x and y, each pair representing the value of a response y for a given value of x. Plotting these points on a rectangular coordinate system, a scatter diagram is created, graphically describing the relationship between y and x.

Someone might say that these points appear to cluster around a "trend line." That is, the points appear to be deviations about a straight line, which can be represented by the linear equation

$$y = \beta_0 + \beta_1 x$$

This straight line is called the *regression line,* and an approximation for this line can be obtained in several ways.

2. Suppose that the set of n points (x, y), when plotted in a scatter diagram produce the following results.

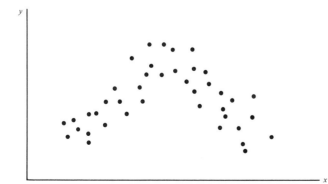

curve
is not
should not

The "trend line" or regression line that best describes this data is no longer a line in the strict sense of the word, but is in fact a _____ . The relationship between y and x (is, is not) linear but is described as curvilinear. In this case, a linear equation of the form $y = \beta_0 + \beta_1 x$ (should, should not) be used to describe the relationship between y and x.

Let us assume that the n data points are as described in part 1, and that a line of the form $y = \beta_0 + \beta_1 x$ represents the regression line. One method used to approximate this line is to draw a *freehand regression line,* obtained by passing a ruler through the n points until it appears to "fit well" by minimizing the distances of the points from the fitted line.

Example 10.2

The following are 5 data points observed as the outcome of an experiment. Plot these points on a scatter diagram and draw a freehand regression line.

x	2	3	5	7	9
y	1	3	4	7	10

Solution

1. The five points are graphed on the rectangular coordinate system below.

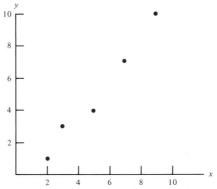

2. The relationship appears to be linear and a freehand regression line can be superimposed on the graph.

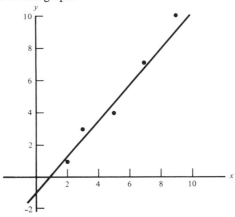

3. For this freehand line, when $x = 0$, $y \approx -1$. Hence, the y intercept is $\beta_0 = -1$. When $x = 2$, $y \approx 1.3$, while when $x = 4$, $y \approx 3.5$. The change in y for a two-unit change in x is $3.5 - 1.3 = 2.2$. Hence, the slope, which represents the change in y for a one-unit change in x, is $\beta_1 = 2.2/2 = 1.1$.
4. The freehand regression line is approximately,

$$y = -1 + 1.1x$$

10.3 Method of Least Squares

A statistical method used for estimating β_0 and β_1 in the regression line is to find an estimated line

$$\hat{y} = \hat{\beta}_0 + \hat{\beta}_1 x$$

that in some sense minimizes the deviations of the observed values of y from the fitted line. If the deviation of an observed value from the fitted value is $(y - \hat{y})$, we define the best estimated line as one that minimizes the sum of squares of the deviations of the observed values of y from the fitted values of y. The quantity

$$\Sigma(y - \hat{y})^2$$

represents the sum of squares of deviations of the observed values of y from the fitted values and is called the sum of squares for error (SSE):

$$\text{SSE} = \Sigma(y - \hat{y})^2 = \Sigma[y - (\hat{\beta}_0 + \hat{\beta}_1 x)]^2$$

The values of $\hat{\beta}_0$ and $\hat{\beta}_1$ are determined mathematically so that SSE will be minimum.

This process of minimization is called the *method of least squares* and produces estimates of β_0 and β_1. The least squares estimates of β_1 and β_0 are

$$\hat{\beta}_1 = S_{xy}/S_{xx} \quad \text{and} \quad \hat{\beta}_0 = \bar{y} - \hat{\beta}_1 \bar{x}$$

where

$$S_{xy} = \Sigma xy - \frac{(\Sigma x)(\Sigma y)}{n} \quad \text{and} \quad S_{xx} = \Sigma x^2 - \frac{(\Sigma x)^2}{n}$$

and $\bar{x}$ and $\bar{y}$ denote the sample means for the x and y observations, respectively.

Example 10.3
The following are the data points given in example 10.2. In this chapter we will use this example to illustrate each type of problem encountered. Be ready to

refer to the information tabulated on this page. For the following data, find the best fitting line, $\hat{y} = \hat{\beta}_0 + \hat{\beta}_1 x$:

x	y	x^2	y^2	xy
2	1	4	1	2
3	3	9	9	9
5	4	25	16	20
7	7	49	49	49
9	10	81	100	90
Sum _____	_____	168	175	170
$\bar{x} = $ _____	$\bar{y} = $ _____			

26; 25

5.2; 5

Solution

1. First find all the sums needed in the computations.

$$S_{xy} = \Sigma xy - \frac{(\Sigma x)(\Sigma y)}{n}$$

26; 25

$$= 170 - \frac{(\underline{\hspace{1cm}})(\underline{\hspace{1cm}})}{5}$$

130

$$= 170 - \underline{\hspace{1.5cm}}$$

40

$$= \underline{\hspace{1.5cm}}$$

$$S_{xx} = \Sigma x^2 - \frac{(\Sigma x)^2}{n}$$

168

$$= \underline{\hspace{1.5cm}} - \frac{(26)^2}{5}$$

168

$$= \underline{\hspace{1.5cm}} - 135.2$$

32.8

$$= \underline{\hspace{1.5cm}}$$

2.

1.2195

$$\hat{\beta}_1 = \frac{S_{xy}}{S_{xx}} = \frac{4.0}{32.8} = \underline{\hspace{1.5cm}}$$

3. $\hat{\beta}_0 = \bar{y} - \hat{\beta}_1 \bar{x}$

   $= ($ _____ $) - 1.22($ _____ $)$ 5; 5.2

   $= ($ _____ $) - ($ _____ $)$ 5; 6.34140

   $= -1.34140$

4. Using two-decimal accuracy, the best-fitting line is

   $\hat{y} = $ _____ $-1.34 + 1.22x$

We can now use the equation

   $\hat{y} = -1.34 + 1.22x$

to predict values of _____ for values of x in the interval $2 \leqslant x \leqslant 9$. y

Example 10.4

The following experiment was undertaken in order to determine whether there is a relationship between time spent with a student (y) and the number of academic counselors (x) on duty. Ten students with similar problems were observed. The following data represent the time spent with each student (y) and the number of counselors on duty at the time of the interview.

x (number of counselors)	y (time in minutes)
3	12
7	18
6	15
8	20
9	21
11	25
10	19
12	27
14	29
15	30

Fit a least squares line to these data.

Solution

1. Display the data in a tabulated form that will allow for computation of the required arithmetic quantities.

x	y	x^2	xy	y^2
3	12	9	36	144
7	18	49	126	324
6	15	36	90	225
8	20	64	160	400
9	21	81	189	441
11	25	121	275	625
10	19	100	190	361
12	27	144	324	729
14	29	196	406	841
15	30	225	450	900
		1025	2246	4990

95; 216

9.5 $\bar{x} = \underline{\hspace{2cm}}$

21.6 $\bar{y} = \underline{\hspace{2cm}}$

2. Now compute S_{xy} and S_{xx}.

$$S_{xy} = \Sigma xy - \frac{(\Sigma x)(\Sigma y)}{n}$$

2246 $$= \underline{\hspace{2cm}} - \frac{(95)(216)}{10}$$

2052 $$= 2246 - \underline{\hspace{2cm}}$$

194 $$= \underline{\hspace{2cm}}$$

$$S_{xx} = \Sigma x^2 - \frac{(\Sigma x)^2}{n}$$

1025 $$= \underline{\hspace{2cm}} - \frac{(95)^2}{10}$$

902.5 $$= 1025 - \underline{\hspace{2cm}}$$

122.5 $$= \underline{\hspace{2cm}}$$

3. To find the slope, $\hat{\beta}_1$, use

1.58367 $$\hat{\beta}_1 = \frac{S_{xy}}{S_{xx}} = \frac{194}{122.5} = \underline{\hspace{2cm}}$$

Correct to two decimal places, we will take

$$\hat{\beta}_1 = \underline{\hspace{2cm}}$$

1.58

To find the intercept, $\hat{\beta}_0$, use

$$\hat{\beta}_0 = \bar{y} - \hat{\beta}_1 \bar{x}$$

$$= \underline{\hspace{2cm}} - (1.58367)(\underline{\hspace{2cm}})$$

21.6; 9.5

$$= 21.6 - \underline{\hspace{2cm}}$$

15.04487

$$= \underline{\hspace{2cm}}$$

6.55513

which, correct to two decimal places, is

$$\hat{\beta}_0 = \underline{\hspace{2cm}}$$

6.56

4. Therefore the best-fitting line is given by

$$\hat{y} = \underline{\hspace{3cm}}$$

6.56 + 1.58x

The equation $\hat{y} = 6.56 + 1.58x$ can be used to predict values for y (the counselling time in minutes) for values of x (the number of _____) between 3 and 15. We see from our fitted equation that counselling time (increases, decreases) _____ minutes for every one unit increase in x (i.e., every time a counselor is added). If 13 counselors were employed, the predicted counselling time would be $\hat{y} = \hat{\beta}_0 + \hat{\beta}_1 x = $ _____ + 1.58 (_____) = _____ .

counselors

increases; 1.58

6.56; 13
27.1

Self-Correcting Exercises 10A

1. The registrar at a small university noted that the preenrollment figures and the actual enrollment figures for the past 6 years (in hundreds of students) were as shown here:

x, preenrollment	30	35	42	48	50	51
y, actual enrollment	33	41	46	52	59	55

a. Plot these data. Does it appear that a linear relationship exists between x and y?
b. Find the least squares line $\hat{y} = \hat{\beta}_0 + \hat{\beta}_1 x$.
c. Using the least squares line, predict the actual number of students enrolled if the preenrollment figure is 5000 students.

2. An entomologist, interested in predicting cotton harvest using the number of cotton bolls per quadrate counted during the middle of the growing season, collected the following data, where y is the yield in bales of cotton per field quadrate and x is hundreds of cotton bolls per quadrate counted during midseason:

y	21	17	20	19	15	23	20
x	5.5	2.8	4.7	4.3	3.7	6.1	4.5

a. Fit the least squares line $\hat{y} = \hat{\beta}_0 + \hat{\beta}_1 x$ using these data.
b. Plot the least squares line and the actual data on the same graph. Comment on the adequacy of the least squares predictor to describe these data.

3. Refer to exercise 2. The same entomologist also had available a measure of the number of damaging insects present per quadrate during a critical time in the development of the cotton plants. The data follow.

y, yield	21	17	20	19	15	23	20
x, insects	11	20	13	12	18	10	12

a. Fit the least squares line to these data.
b. Plot the least squares line and the actual data points on the same graph. Does it appear that the prediction line adequately describes the relationship between yield y and the number of insects present x?

10.4 Inferences Concerning the Slope of the Line, β_1

The slope β_1 is the average increase in _____ for a one-unit increase in _____. The question of the existence of a linear relationship between x and y must be phrased in terms of the slope β_1. If no linear relationship exists between x and y, then $\beta_1 = 0$. Hence a test of the existence of a *linear* relationship between x and y is given as $H_0 : \beta_1 = $ _____ versus $H_a : \beta_1 \neq$ _____.
Assume that, for each fixed value of x, there is a population of y values that can be represented by a normal distribution. Further suppose that for every fixed value of x, the variance of this normal distribution is equal to a common value, σ^2. The distributions of y for three fixed values of x are visually represented below.

y
x

$0; 0$

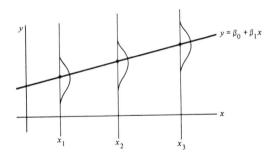

The following test statistics can be constructed using the above assumptions:

1. $z = \dfrac{\hat{\beta}_1 - \beta_1}{\sigma/\sqrt{S_{xx}}}$ if σ^2 is known

2. $t = \dfrac{\hat{\beta}_1 - \beta_1}{s/\sqrt{S_{xx}}}$ if s^2 is used to estimate σ^2

where $s^2 = \dfrac{S_{yy} - \hat{\beta}_1 S_{xy}}{n-2}$ and $S_{yy} = \Sigma y^2 - \dfrac{(\Sigma y)^2}{n}$

Since σ^2 is rarely known, we can test for a significant linear relationship using the statistic given in 2, which has a Student's t distribution with _____ $n-2$ degrees of freedom. A test of the hypothesis $H_0 : \beta_1 = 0$ versus $H_a : \beta_1 \neq 0$ is given as follows:

1. $H_0 : \beta_1 = 0$

2. $H_a : \beta_1 \neq 0$

3. Test statistic:

$$t = \dfrac{\hat{\beta}_1 - (0)}{s/\sqrt{S_{xx}}}$$

4. Rejection region: Reject H_0 if $|t| > t_{\alpha/2}$ based on $(n-2)$ degrees freedom.

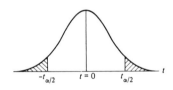

Example 10.5

For the data in example 10.3, test the hypothesis that there is no linear relation-ship between x and y at the $\alpha = .05$ level.

Solution

We will first need to calculate s^2, the estimate of σ^2. Using the more accurate calculation of $\hat{\beta}_1$,

$$S_{yy} = \Sigma y^2 - \frac{(\Sigma y)^2}{n}$$

25

$$= 175 - \frac{(\underline{\hspace{1cm}})^2}{5}$$

50

$$= \underline{\hspace{1.5cm}}$$

and

$$s^2 = \frac{S_{yy} - \hat{\beta}_1 S_{xy}}{n - 2}$$

$$= \frac{50 - 1.2195(40)}{3}$$

$$= \frac{1.2195}{3}$$

$$= .4065$$

0

1. $H_0: \beta_1 = \underline{\hspace{1.5cm}}$

0

2. $H_a: \beta_1 \neq \underline{\hspace{1.5cm}}$

3. Test statistic:

$$t = \frac{\hat{\beta}_1 - (0)}{s/\sqrt{S_{xx}}}$$

4. Rejection region: With 3 degrees of freedom, we will reject H_0 if $|t| > t_{.025} =$

3.182

$\underline{\hspace{1.5cm}}$.

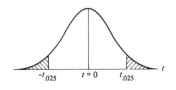

5. Calculate the statistic:

$$t = \frac{1.2195 - 0}{\sqrt{.4065}/\sqrt{32.8}} = \frac{1.2195}{\underline{\hspace{1.5cm}}} = \underline{\hspace{1.5cm}}$$

.111; 10.95

6. Since 10.95 is larger than the critical value of $t =$ _____, we (reject, do not reject) H_0 and conclude that there (is, is not) a linear relationship between x and y.

3.182; reject
is

Confidence Interval for β_1

If x increases one unit, what is the predicted change in y? Since $\hat{\beta}_1$ is an estimator with average value β_1 and has a normal distribution, the t statistic, based on $(n - 2)$ degrees of freedom, can be used to derive the confidence interval estimator for the slope β_1:

$$\hat{\beta}_1 \pm t \frac{s}{\sqrt{S_{xx}}}$$

where t corresponding to a 90%, 95% or 99% confidence interval is found in Table 2, indexing $(n - 2)$ degrees of freedom and $a = .05, .025,$ or $.005$.

Example 10.6

Find a 95% confidence interval for the average change in y for an increase of one unit in x.

Solution

1. For a 95% confidence interval, use Table 2, indexing $n - 2 =$ _____,
   $a =$ _____, so that $t =$ _____.

3
.025; 3.182

2. $$\hat{\beta}_1 \pm t \frac{s}{\sqrt{S_{xx}}}$$

$$1.22 \pm (\underline{\hspace{1.5cm}}) \frac{\sqrt{.4065}}{\sqrt{32.8}}$$

3.182

$$1.22 \pm (\underline{\hspace{1.5cm}})$$

.35

3. A 95% confidence interval for β_1 is (_____, _____).

.87; 1.57

Points Concerning Interpretation of Results

If the test $H_0 : \beta_1 = 0$ is performed and H_0 is *not rejected,* this (does, does not) mean that x and y are *not related,* since

does not

1. a type _____ error may have been committed, or

II

linearly

cannot

inaccurate

extrapolation

2. x and y may be related, but not _____. For example, the true relationship may be of the form $y = \beta_0 + \beta_1 x + \beta_2 x^2$.
If the test $H_0 : \beta_1 = 0$ is performed and H_0 is *rejected*,
1. we (can, cannot) say that x and y are solely linearly related, since there may be other terms $(x^2 \text{ or } x^3)$ that have not been included in our model; and
2. we should not conclude that a *causal* relationship exists between x and y, since the related changes we observe in x and y may actually be *caused* by an unmeasured third variable, say z.

Consider the problem where the true relationship between x and y is a "curve" rather than a straight line. Suppose we fitted a straight line to the data for values of x between a and b.

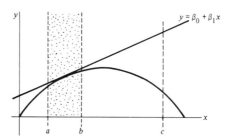

Using $\hat{y} = \hat{\beta}_0 + \hat{\beta}_1 x$ to predict values of y for $a \leqslant x \leqslant b$ would result in quite an accurate prediction. However, if the prediction line were used to predict y for the value $x = c$, the prediction would be highly _____. Although the line adequately describes the indicated trend in the region $a \leqslant x \leqslant b$, there is no justification for assuming that the line would fit equally well for values of x outside the region $a \leqslant x \leqslant b$. The process of predicting outside the region of experimentation is called _____. As our example shows, an experimenter should *not* extrapolate unless he or she is willing to assume the consequences of *gross errors*.

Self-Correcting Exercises 10B

1. Refer to exercise 1, Self-Correcting Exercises 10A. Calculate s^2, and s for these data.
   a. Test the hypothesis that there is no linear relationship between actual and preenrollment figures. (Use $\alpha = .05$.)
   b. Estimate the average increase in actual enrollment for an increase of 100 in preenrolled students with a 95% confidence interval.
2. Refer to exercise 2, Self-Correcting Exercises 10A. Calculate s^2, and s for these data and test for a significant linear relationship between yield and number of bolls. (Use $\alpha = .05$.)
3. Refer to exercise 3, Self-Correcting Exercises 10A. Test for a significant linear relationship between yield and the number of insects present. (Use $\alpha = .05$.)

10.5 The Coefficient of Linear Correlation

The Pearson product moment coefficient of correlation is a measure of the strength of the _____ relationship between two variables and is independent of the respective scales of measurement. The sample coefficient of correlation used to estimate ρ, the population coefficient, is given as

$$\hat{\rho} = \frac{\Sigma(x - \bar{x})(y - \bar{y})}{\sqrt{\Sigma(x - \bar{x})^2 \Sigma(y - \bar{y})^2}}$$

where $-1 \leqslant \hat{\rho} \leqslant 1$.

The computational formula for $\hat{\rho}$ is

$$\hat{\rho} = \frac{S_{xy}}{\sqrt{S_{xx}S_{yy}}}$$

Examine the forms for $\hat{\rho}$ given above and note the following:
1. The denominator of $\hat{\rho}$ is the square root of the product of two positive quantities and will always be _____.
2. The numerator of $\hat{\rho}$ is identical to the numerator used to calculate _____, whose denominator is also always positive.
3. Hence _____ and $\hat{\rho}$ will always have the same algebraic sign.
   a. When $\hat{\beta}_1 > 0$, then $\hat{\rho}$ _____.
   b. When $\hat{\beta}_1 = 0$, then $\hat{\rho}$ _____.
   c. When $\hat{\beta}_1 < 0$, then $\hat{\rho}$ _____.
When $\hat{\rho} > 0$, there is a _____ linear correlation; when $\hat{\rho} < 0$, there is a _____ linear correlation; when $\hat{\rho} = 0$, there is _____ linear correlation. See the following examples:

right margin answers: linear; positive; $\hat{\beta}_1$; $\hat{\beta}_1$; >0; $=0$; <0; positive; negative; no

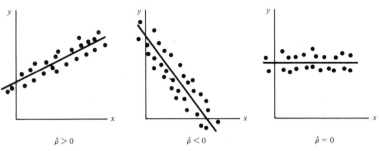

$\hat{\rho} > 0$ $\hat{\rho} < 0$ $\hat{\rho} = 0$

Notice that both $\hat{\rho}$ and $\hat{\beta}_1$ measure the linear relationship between x and y. While $\hat{\rho}$ is independent of the scale of measurement, $\hat{\beta}_1$ retains the measurement units for both x and y, since $\hat{\beta}_1$ is the number of units increase in _____ for a one-unit increase in _____. When should the investigator use $\hat{\rho}$, and when should a least squares estimate of β_1 be used? Although the situation is not always clear-cut, $\hat{\rho}$ is used when either x or y can be considered as the random

right margin: y; x

variable of interest (i.e., when x and y are both random), while regression estimates and confidence intervals are appropriate when one variable, say x, is not
random and the other (y) is random.

Example 10.7

Two personnel evaluation techniques are available. The first requires a 2-hour
test-interview session, while the second can be completed in less than an hour.
A high correlation between test scores would indicate that the second test,
which is shorter to use, could replace the 2-hour test and hence save time and
money. The following data give the scores on test I (x) and test II (y) for $n =$
15 job applicants. Find the coefficient of correlation for the following pairs of
scores:

Applicant	Test I (x)	Test II (y)
1	75	38
2	89	56
3	60	35
4	71	45
5	92	59
6	105	70
7	55	31
8	87	52
9	73	48
10	77	41
11	84	51
12	91	58
13	75	45
14	82	49
15	76	47

Solution

1. As with a regression problem, we need all the summations as given in section
   10.3. Using a similar tabulation (or a calculator), find the following
   summations:

1,192; 725

$$\Sigma x = \underline{\hspace{2cm}} \qquad \Sigma y = \underline{\hspace{2cm}}$$

$$\Sigma x^2 = 96,990 \qquad \Sigma y^2 = 36,461$$

59,324

$$\Sigma xy = \underline{\hspace{2cm}}$$

2. To use the computational formula for $\hat{\rho}$, we need the following:

$$S_{xy} = \Sigma xy - \frac{(\Sigma x)(\Sigma y)}{n}$$

$$= 59{,}324 - \frac{(\underline{\hspace{2cm}})\,(\underline{\hspace{2cm}})}{15}$$

1,192; 725

$$= \underline{\hspace{2cm}}$$

1,710.6667

$$S_{xx} = \Sigma x^2 - \frac{(\Sigma x)^2}{n}$$

$$= 96{,}990 - \frac{(\underline{\hspace{2cm}})^2}{15}$$

1,192

$$= 2{,}265.7333,$$

$$S_{yy} = \Sigma y^2 - \frac{(\Sigma y)^2}{n}$$

$$= 36{,}461 - \frac{(\underline{\hspace{2cm}})^2}{15}$$

725

$$= 1{,}419.3333$$

Then

$$\hat{\rho} = \frac{S_{xy}}{\sqrt{S_{xx}S_{yy}}}$$

$$= \frac{(\underline{\hspace{2cm}})}{\sqrt{(2{,}265.7333)\,(1{,}419.3333)}}$$

1,710.6667

$$= \frac{(\underline{\hspace{2cm}})}{1{,}793.1154}$$

1,710.6667

$$= \underline{\hspace{2cm}}$$

.9540

3. Since the correlation coefficient has a maximum value of 1 and a minimum value of –1, it would appear that the correlation between these two test scores is quite strong, with the relationship being a _____ linear one, as indicated by the sign of the correlation coefficient. In other words, a high score on test I would predict a _____ score on test II, or a low score on test I would predict a _____ score on test II.

positive

high
low

What more can be gleaned from knowing the value of $\hat{\rho}$? How can one assess the strength of the linear relationship of two variables? If $\hat{\rho} = 0$, it is fairly obvious that there appears to be no linear relationship between x and y. To evaluate non-zero values of $\hat{\rho}$, let us consider two possible predictors of y.

1. If the x variate were not measured, we would be forced to use $\bar{y}$ to predict the response y.
2. If the x variate is measured, we can use the estimate of the regression line, $\hat{y} = \hat{\beta}_0 + \hat{\beta}_1 x$, to predict the response y. It can be shown that the quantity

$\hat{\rho}^2$ = ratio of the reduction in the sum of squares achieved by using the linear model to the total sum of squares about the sample mean which would be used as a predictor of y if x were ignored.

A more understandable way of saying the same thing is to note that $\hat{\rho}^2$ represents the amount of variability in y that is accounted for by knowing x. Thus we see that to evaluate a correlation coefficient $\hat{\rho}$, we should examine $\hat{\rho}^2$ to interpret the strength of the linear relationship between x and y. The quantity $\hat{\rho}^2$ is often called the *coefficient of determination*.

For our example, the value of $\hat{\rho}$ was found to be $\hat{\rho} = .9540$; therefore, $\hat{\rho}^2 =$

.9101

91%

_____ . Hence we have reduced the variability of our predictor by _____ by knowing the value of x.

Test of Hypothesis Concerning ρ, the Population Correlation Coefficient
It is possible not only to estimate the population correlation coefficient, ρ, but also to test an hypothesis concerning the value of ρ. An experimenter is often interested in knowing whether or not a significant correlation exists between the variables x and y. That is, it is necessary to test the hypothesis

$$H_0: \quad \rho = 0$$

$$H_a: \quad \rho \neq 0$$

Possibly, the experimenter might be interested in a directional alternative which suggests positive ($\rho > 0$) or negative ($\rho < 0$) correlation. The test of hypothesis appropriate for this situation is exactly equivalent to the test of $H_0: \beta_1 = 0$ presented in section 10.4 and is based on a similar set of assumptions. The test is given below:

1. $\qquad H_0: \quad \rho = 0$

2. Appropriate one- or two-tailed alternative hypothesis.

3. Test statistic:

$$t = \hat{\rho} \sqrt{\frac{n-2}{1-\hat{\rho}^2}}$$

4. For a specified value of α and $(n - 2)$ degrees of freedom, the appropriate one- or two-tailed rejection region is found using Table 2 of the appendix.

Example 10.8
For the data given in example 10.2, calculate $\hat{\rho}$ and test for significant correlation at the $\alpha = .05$ level of significance.

Solution
From example 10.3, $S_{xy} = 40, S_{xx} = 32.8, S_{yy} = 50$. Hence,

$$\hat{\rho} = \frac{S_{xy}}{\sqrt{S_{xx}S_{yy}}}$$

$$= \frac{40}{\sqrt{32.8(50)}}$$

$$= \frac{40}{40.4969} = .9877$$

The test of hypothesis is as follows:

1. $\quad H_0: \ \rho = 0$

2. $\quad H_a: \ \rho \neq 0$

3. Test statistic:

$$t = \hat{\rho} \sqrt{\frac{n - 2}{1 - \hat{\rho}^2}}$$

$$= .9877 \sqrt{\frac{\underline{\hspace{1cm}}}{1 - (\underline{\hspace{1cm}})^2}} \qquad \qquad \begin{array}{l} 3 \\ .9877 \end{array}$$

$$= .9877 \sqrt{\underline{\hspace{1cm}}} \qquad \qquad 122.7059$$

$$= 10.\underline{\hspace{1cm}} \qquad \qquad 94$$

Note that except for rounding error, this is exactly the same value for t as was given in example 10.5, in which we tested $H_0: \beta_1 = 0$ against $H_a: \beta_1 \neq 0$.

4. Rejection Region: With 3 degrees of freedom, we will reject H_0 if $|t| > t_{.025}$
= \underline{\hspace{1cm}}. $\qquad \qquad$ 3.182

5. Since $t = 10.94$ (falls, does not fall) in the rejection region, we (reject, do not reject) H_0. There (is, is not) significant correlation between x and y. $\qquad$ falls; reject

is

Self-Correcting Exercises 10C

1. Refer to exercise 2, Self-Correcting Exercises 10A.
   a. Find the correlation between the number of bolls and the yield of cotton.
   b. Find the coefficient of determination $\hat{\rho}^2$, and explain its significance in using the number of cotton bolls to predict the yield of cotton.
   c. Test to see if there is a significant positive correlation between x and y. (Use $\alpha = .05$.)
2. Refer to exercise 3, Self-Correcting Exercises 10A.
   a. Find the value of $\hat{\rho}^2$ and $\hat{\rho}$ for these data and explain the value of using the number of damaging insects present to predict cotton yield.
   b. Compare the values of $\hat{\rho}^2$ using these two predictors of cotton yield. Which predictor would you prefer?
3. The data in exercises 2 and 3, Self-Correcting Exercises 10A, are related in that for each field quadrate, the yield, the number of bolls, and the number of damaging insects were simultaneously recorded. Using this fact, calculate the correlation between the number of cotton bolls and the number of insects present for the seven field quadrates. Does this value of $\hat{\rho}$ explain in any way the similarity of results when using the predictor in exercise 2 and that in exercise 3?

10.6 Multiple Regression

We have examined estimation, testing, and prediction techniques for the situation in which y, the response of interest, was linearly related to an independent variable x. In this situation, the prediction equation was

$$\hat{y} = \hat{\beta}_0 + \hat{\beta}_1 x$$

where $\hat{\beta}_0$ and $\hat{\beta}_1$ were obtained using the method of least squares. In this section, we extend these techniques to the more general situation in which the response y is linearly related to one or more independent variables. In particular, consider the dependent variable y and k independent variables, $x_1, x_2, \ldots, x_k$. We will use sample data to obtain a prediction equation of the form

$$\hat{y} = \hat{\beta}_0 + \hat{\beta}_1 x_1 + \hat{\beta}_2 x_2 + \ldots + \hat{\beta}_k x_k$$

Estimates of the unknown parameters in the model are found by using the method of least squares. Using this method, the estimates $\hat{\beta}_0, \hat{\beta}_1, \ldots, \hat{\beta}_k$ are

minimize

chosen so as to _____ the quantity

$$SSE = \Sigma(y - \hat{y})^2 = \Sigma(y - \hat{\beta}_0 - \hat{\beta}_1 x_1 - \ldots - \hat{\beta}_k x_k)^2$$

normal

This minimization technique leads to a set of equations called the _____

_____ with $\hat{\beta}_0, \hat{\beta}_1, \ldots, \hat{\beta}_k$ as the unknown quantities. These equations can be solved simultaneously to find the least squares estimates of β_0, $\beta_1, \ldots, \beta_k$. However, this is beyond the scope of this text. Packaged computer programs can be used to find $\hat{\beta}_0, \hat{\beta}_1, \ldots, \hat{\beta}_k$; and the prediction equation can then be used to predict y for given values of $x_1, x_2, x_3, \ldots, x_k$.

equations

Example 10.9
In order to study the relationship of advertising and capital investment on corporate profits, the following data, recorded in units of $100,000, was collected for ten medium-sized firms within the same year. The variable y represents profit for the year, x_1 represents capital investment, and x_2 represents advertising expenditures.

y	x_1	x_2
15	25	4
16	1	5
2	6	3
3	30	1
12	29	2
1	20	0
16	12	4
18	15	5
13	6	4
2	16	2

a. Using the computer printout shown below, write the prediction equation for these data in the form

$$\hat{y} = \hat{\beta}_0 + \hat{\beta}_1 x_1 + \hat{\beta}_2 x_2$$

b. Use the prediction equation to estimate yearly corporate profits for a medium sized firm whose capital investment was $2,200,000 and whose advertising expenditure was $400,000.

MULTIPLE R   .9072
R SQUARE   .8230
STD. ERROR OF EST.   3.3033

ANALYSIS OF VARIANCE

	DF	SUM OF SQUARES	MEAN SQUARE	F RATIO
REGRESSION	2	355.2151	177.6076	16.2762
RESIDUAL	7	76.3849	10.9121	

INDIVIDUAL ANALYSIS OF VARIABLES

VARIABLE	COEFFICIENT	STD. ERROR	F VALUE
(CONSTANT	-8.1770)		
CAPITAL	.2921	.1357	4.6335
ADVERTISING	4.4343	.8002	30.7048

Solution

a. At this point we are interested in that portion of the printout labeled INDIVIDUAL ANALYSIS OF VARIABLES. The first column identifies the estimated coefficients and the second column their values. Thus, the intercept, or CONSTANT, is estimated to be $\hat{\beta}_0 = -8.1770$, the partial regression coefficient corresponding to the variable CAPITAL (x_1) is $\hat{\beta}_1 = .2921$, and the partial regression coefficient corresponding to ADVERTISING (x_2) is $\hat{\beta}_2 = 4.4343$. The least squares prediction equation is

-8.1770

$$\hat{y} = \underline{\hspace{1.5cm}} + .2921x_1 + 4.3434x_2$$

b. The prediction equation is given as

$$\hat{y} = -8.1770 + .2921x_1 + 4.4343x_2$$

Since x_1, capital investment, and x_2, advertising expenditure, were given in units of $100,000, the values to be entered into the prediction equation are

22; 4

$$x_1 = \underline{\hspace{1.5cm}} \text{ and } x_2 = \underline{\hspace{1.5cm}}. \text{ Therefore}$$

22; 4

$$\hat{y} = -8.1770 + .2921(\underline{\hspace{1.5cm}}) + 4.4343(\underline{\hspace{1.5cm}})$$

6.4262; 17.7372

$$= -8.1770 + \underline{\hspace{1.5cm}} + \underline{\hspace{1.5cm}}$$

15.9864

$$= \underline{\hspace{1.5cm}}$$

$100,000

To find the actual profit, multiply 15.9864 by _____ to find that when capital investment is $2,200,000 and advertising expenditure is $400,000,

$1,598,640

profit is estimated to be _____.

Note that we have presented only the very basics in terms of prediction for a multivariable situation. Estimation and hypothesis testing are available as well as methods for placing bounds on the goodness of various prediction techniques. The interested reader should refer to textbooks listed at the end of chapter 10 in your text.

EXERCISES

1. For the following equations (i) give the y intercept, (ii) give the slope, and (iii) graph the line corresponding to the equation:

a. $y = 3x - 2$. d. $3x + 2y = 5$.

b. $2y = 4x$. e. $y = 2$.

c. $-y = .5 + x$.

2. The following data were obtained in an experiment relating the dependent variable y (texture of strawberries) with x (coded storage temperature):

x	-2	-2	0	2	2
y	4.0	3.5	2.0	.5	.0

a. Find the least squares line for the data.
b. Plot the data points and graph the least squares line as a check on your calculations.
c. Do the data indicate that texture and storage temperature are linearly related? (Use $\alpha = .05$.)
d. Calculate $\hat{\rho}$. Of what value is the linear model in increasing the accuracy of prediction as compared to the predictor $\bar{y}$?

3. In addition to increasingly large bounds on error, why should an experimenter refrain from predicting y for values of x outside the experimental region?

4. What happens if the coefficient of linear correlation $\hat{\rho}$ assumes the value 1?

5. An agricultural experimenter, investigating the effect of the amount of nitrogen x applied in 100 pounds per acre on the yield of oats y, measured in bushels per acre, collected the following data:

x	1	2	3	4
y	22	38	57	68
	19	41	54	65

a. Fit a least squares line to the data.
b. Is there sufficient evidence to indicate that the yield of oats is linearly related to the amount of nitrogen applied? (Use $\alpha = .05$.)
c. Predict the average increase in yield for an increase of 100 pounds of nitrogen.
d. Calculate $\hat{\rho}$ and explain its significance in terms of predicting y, the yield of oats. Is there a significant correlation between x and y? (Use $\alpha = .05$.)

6. In an industrial process, the yield y is thought to be linearly related to temperature x. The following coded data are available:

Temperature	0	.5	1.5	2.0	2.5
Yield	7.2	8.1	9.8	11.3	12.9
	6.9	8.4	10.1	11.7	13.2

a. Find the least squares line for these data.

b. Plot the points and graph the line. Is your calculated line reasonable?

c. Calculate s^2.

d. Do the data indicate a linear relationship between yield and temperature at the $\alpha = .01$ level of significance?

e. Calculate $\hat{\rho}$, the coefficient of linear correlation. Is there a significant correlation between x and y? (Use $\alpha = .05$.)

f. Calculate $\hat{\rho}^2$ and interpret its significance in predicting the yield y.

g. Predict the particular value of y for a coded temperature $x = 1$.

7. A horticulturist devised a scale to measure the viability of roses that were packaged and stored for varying periods of time before transplanting. y represents the viability measurement and x represents the length of time in days that the plant is packaged and stored before transplanting.

x	5	10	15	20	25
y	15.3	13.6	9.8	5.5	1.8
	16.8	13.8	8.7	4.7	1.0

a. Fit a least squares line to the data.

b. Calculate s^2 for the data.

c. Is there sufficient evidence to indicate that a linear relationship exists between freshness and storage time? (Use $\alpha = .05$.)

d. Estimate the mean rate of change in freshness for a 1-day increase in storage time using a 95% confidence interval.

e. Predict the expected freshness measurement for a storage time of 14 days.

f. Of what value is the linear model in preference to $\bar{y}$ in predicting freshness?

8. A study was conducted to determine the effects of sleep deprivation on subjects' scores on a standardized exam. The amount of sleep deprivation varied over 16, 20, 24, 28, and 32 hours without sleep. A total of 10 subjects participated in the study, 2 at each level of sleep deprivation. After each subject's specified period of sleep deprivation, the subject was administered the standardized examination and the percentile score on the exam was determined. The results were as follows:

	Subject									
	1	*2*	*3*	*4*	*5*	*6*	*7*	*8*	*9*	*10*
No. hours without sleep (x)	16	16	20	20	24	24	28	28	32	32
Score on exam (y)	80	72	74	65	68	60	65	56	52	58

a. Fit a least squares line to the data.

b. Plot the points and graph the line. Is your calculated line reasonable?

c. Do the data indicate a linear relationship between number of hours without sleep and exam score? (Use $\alpha = .05$.)

d. Predict the expected score on the exam for a subject denied sleep for 24 hours.

e. Calculate $\hat{\rho}$. Is there a significant correlation between x and y at the .05 level of significance?

Chapter 11

THE DESIGN OF AN EXPERIMENT: GETTING MORE FOR YOUR MONEY

11.1 Introduction

In previous chapters we have used probabilistic concepts to develop methodologies for making inferences about populations in terms of their parameters. The emphasis in these chapters was on the analysis of data after the experiment had been conducted. Now that we have seen how information can be extracted from data, it is natural to ask (1) what factors affect the quantity of information in an experiment and (2) how can knowledge of these factors be used to design better experiments?

The objective of this chapter is to acquaint you with some of these factors and to show, in some simple cases, how the factors can be controlled in order to increase the amount of information that can be extracted from the data. The experiment should be designed to acquire a specified amount of information at a minimum cost.

There are two factors that affect the amount of information in a sample available for making inferences about a population parameter:
1. The sample size (or sizes) used in experimentation
2. The amount of variation in the experimental data
Increasing the sample size or decreasing the amount of variation in the experiment tends to increase the amount of available information.

Example 11.1
Consider the problem of estimating a population mean μ with a 95% confidence interval, given as

$$\bar{y} \pm 1.96 \frac{\sigma}{\sqrt{n}}$$

narrower

The (wider, narrower) this confidence interval is, the more precise is the estimate of μ and the more information we have gleaned from the experiment. Since $z = 1.96$ is a constant, there are two ways in which the width of the confidence interval can be decreased:
1. Increase the sample size n.
2. Decrease the population variance σ^2.

Example 11.2
Consider the problem of estimating the difference between two population means with a 95% confidence interval. Give two ways in which the amount of available information can be increased.

Solution
The 95% confidence interval for $(\mu_1 - \mu_2)$ is

$$(\bar{y}_1 - \bar{y}_2) \pm 1.96 \sqrt{\frac{\sigma_1^2}{n_1} + \frac{\sigma_2^2}{n_2}}$$

_____ .

increased
decreased

The width of the interval will be decreased if
1. one or both of the sample sizes are (decreased, increased),
2. one or both of the population variances are (decreased, increased).
The objective in the design of an experiment is to choose a method of increasing information (1 or 2) that provides the specified amount of information at minimum cost.

increase

In this chapter we will discuss two main topics concerned with the design of an experiment. The first is a method for designing the experiment in an attempt to decrease the variation and hence to (increase, decrease) the amount of information available to the experimenter. The second provides a method for determining the sample size required to obtain a given amount of information.

11.2 The Paired-Difference Experiment: An Example of a Designed Experiment

In many situations an experiment is designed so that a comparison of the effects of two "treatments" is made on the same person, on twin offspring, two animals from the same litter, two pieces of fabric from the same loom, or two plants of the same species grown on adjacent plots. Such experiments are designed so that the pairs of experimental units (people, animals, fabrics, plants) are as much alike as possible. By taking measurements on the two treatments within the relatively homogeneous pairs of experimental units, the difference in the measurements for the two treatments in a pair will primarily reflect the difference between

treatment

_____ means rather than the difference between experimental units. This experimental design reduces the error of comparison and increases the quantity of information in the experiment.

To analyze such an experiment using the techniques of section 9.4 would be incorrect. In planning this type of experiment, we *intentionally violate* the assumption that the measurements are *independent* and hope that this violation will work to our advantage by (increasing, reducing) the variability of the differences of the paired observations. Consider the situation in which two sets of identical twin calves are selected for a diet experiment. One of each set of twins is randomly chosen to be fed diet A while the other is given diet B. At the end of a given period of time, the calves are weighed and the data are presented for analysis.

reducing

	Diet		
Set	A	B	Difference
1	A_1	B_1	$A_1 - B_1$
2	A_2	B_2	$A_2 - B_2$

Now A_1 and B_1 are *not* independent since the calves are identical twins and as such have the same growth trend, weight-gain trend, and so on. Although A_1 could be larger or smaller than B_1, if A_1 were large, we would also expect B_1 to be large. A_2 and B_2 are not independent for the same reason. However, by looking at the differences $(A_1 - B_1)$ and $(A_2 - B_2)$, the characteristics of the twin calves no longer cloud the issue, since these differences would represent the difference due to the effects of the two treatments.

In using a paired-difference design, we analyze the differences of the paired measurements and, in so doing, attempt to *reduce* the *variability* that would be present in two *randomly* selected groups without pairing. A test of the hypothesis that the difference in two population means $(\mu_1 - \mu_2)$ is equal to zero, is equivalent to a test of the hypothesis that the mean of the differences, μ_d, is equal to zero. That is, $H_0: \mu_1 - \mu_2 = 0$ is equivalent to $H_0: \mu_d = 0$.

Example 11.3
To test the results of a conventional versus a new approach to the teaching of reading, 12 pupils were selected and matched according to IQ, age, present reading ability, and so on. One from each of the pairs was assigned to the conventional reading program and the other to the new reading program. At the end of 6 weeks, their progress was measured by a reading test. Do the following data present sufficient evidence to indicate that the new approach is better than the conventional approach at the $\alpha = .05$ level?

Pair	Conventional	New	$d = N - C$
1	78	83	5
2	65	69	4
3	88	87	-1
4	91	93	2
5	72	78	6
6	59	59	0

Find a 95% confidence interval for the difference in mean reading scores.

Solution

We analyze the set of six differences as we would a single set of six measure-ments. The change in notation required is straightforward.

$$\Sigma d = 16 \qquad \Sigma d^2 = 82.$$

The sample mean is

2.67

$$\bar{d} = \frac{1}{6} \Sigma d = \underline{\hspace{2cm}}$$

The sample variance of the differences is

$$s_d^2 = \frac{\Sigma d^2 - (\Sigma d)^2/6}{5}$$

7.8667

$$= \frac{82 - (16)^2/6}{5} = \frac{39.3333}{5} = \underline{\hspace{2cm}}$$

2.80

$$s_d = \sqrt{7.8667} = \underline{\hspace{2cm}}$$

The test is conducted as follows. Remember that $\mu_d = \mu_N - \mu_C$.

1. $\quad H_0: \ \mu_d = 0$

> 0

2. $\quad H_a: \ \mu_d \underline{\hspace{2cm}}$

3. Test statistic:

$$t = \frac{\bar{d} - 0}{s_d/\sqrt{n}}$$

4. Rejection region: Based on 5 degrees of freedom, we will reject H_0 if the ob-served value of t is greater than $t_{.05} = \underline{\hspace{2cm}}$.

2.015

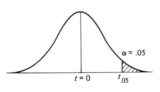

The sample value of t is

$$t = \frac{\bar{d} - 0}{s_d/\sqrt{n}}$$

$$= \frac{- 0}{2.80/\sqrt{6}} = \frac{2.67}{1.14} = \underline{\hspace{1cm}}$$

2.67; 2.34

Since the value of the test statistic is greater than 2.015, we (reject, do not reject) H_0. This sample indicates that the new method appears to be superior to the conventional method at the $\alpha = .05$ level, if we assume that the reading test is a valid criterion upon which to base our judgment.

reject

A 95% confidence interval for $\mu_d = \mu_N - \mu_C$ is

$$\bar{d} \pm t_{.025} \frac{s_d}{\sqrt{n}}$$

Using sample values and $t_{.025} = \underline{\hspace{1cm}}$, we have

2.571

$$2.67 \pm \underline{\hspace{1cm}} (1.14)$$

2.571

$$2.67 \pm \underline{\hspace{1cm}}$$

2.93

With 95% confidence, we estimate that $(\mu_N - \mu_C)$ lies within the interval

$\underline{\hspace{1cm}}$ to $\underline{\hspace{1cm}}$.

-.26; 5.60

Notice that in using a paired-difference analysis, the degrees of freedom for the critical value of t drop from $(2n - 2)$ for an unpaired design to $(n - 1)$ for the paired, a loss of $(2n - 2) - (n - 1) = \underline{\hspace{1cm}}$ degrees of freedom. This results in a (larger, smaller) critical value of t. Therefore, a larger value of the test statistic is needed to reject H_0. Fortunately, *proper* pairing will reduce $\sigma_{\bar{d}}$. Hence the paired-difference experiment results in both a loss and a gain of information. However, the *loss* of $(n - 1)$ degrees of freedom is usually far overshadowed by the gain in information when $\sigma_{\bar{d}}$ is substantially reduced.

$n - 1$

larger

Self-Correcting Exercises 11A

1. The owner of a small manufacturing plant is considering a change in salary base by replacing an hourly wage structure with a per-unit rate. She hopes that such a change will increase the output per worker but has reservations about a possible decrease in quality under the per-unit plan. Before arriving at any decision, she forms 10 pairs of workers so that within each pair the two workers have produced about the same number of items per day and their work has been of comparable quality. From each pair, one worker is ran-

domly selected to be paid as usual and the other is to be paid on a per-unit basis. In addition to the number of items produced, a cumulative quality score for the items produced is kept for each worker. The quality scores follow. (A high score is indicative of high quality.)

	Rate	
Pair	Per Unit	Hourly
1	86	91
2	75	77
3	87	83
4	81	84
5	65	68
6	77	76
7	88	89
8	91	91
9	68	73
10	79	78

Do these data indicate that the average quality for the per-unit production is significantly lower than that based on an hourly wage?

2. Refer to exercise 1. The following data represent the average number of items produced per worker, based on one week's production records:

	Rate	
Pair	Per Unit	Hourly
1	35.8	31.2
2	29.4	27.6
3	31.2	32.2
4	28.6	26.4
5	30.0	29.0
6	32.6	31.4
7	36.8	34.2
8	34.4	31.6
9	29.6	27.6
10	32.8	29.8

a. Estimate the mean difference in average daily output for the two pay scales with a 95% confidence interval.
b. Test the hypothesis that a per-unit pay scale increases production at the .05 level of significance.

3. Eight subjects were asked to perform a simple puzzle-assembly task under normal conditions and under conditions of stress. During the stress condition, the subjects were told that a mild shock would be delivered 3 minutes after the start of the experiment and every 30 seconds thereafter until the task was completed. Blood pressure readings were taken under both conditions. The following data represents the highest reading during the experiment.

Subject	Normal	Stress
1	126	130
2	117	118
3	115	125
4	118	120
5	118	121
6	128	125
7	125	130
8	120	120

Do the data present sufficient evidence to indicate higher blood pressure under conditions of stress? (Use $\alpha = .01$.)

11.3 Choosing the Sample Size to Estimate μ or p

One of the first steps in planning an experiment is deciding on the quantity of information that we wish to buy. At first glance it would seem difficult to specify a measure of the quantity of information in a sample relevant to a parameter of interest. However, such a practical measure is available in the bound on the error of estimation for the parameter.

The larger the sample size, the greater will be the amount of information contained in the sample. This intuitively appealing fact is evident upon examination of the large sample bounds on error for a population mean μ or a population parameter p.

1. The bound on error for μ is _____.

$$2\frac{\sigma}{\sqrt{n}}$$

2. The bound on error for p is _____.

$$2\sqrt{\frac{pq}{n}}$$

Notice that both of these bounds on error are inversely proportional to the square root of the _____ _____. That is, by choosing a large enough value for n, the bound on error can be made as small as necessary. Recall that the bound on the error of estimation is the largest possible difference between the estimator ($\bar{y}$ or $\hat{p}$) and the parameter to be estimated (μ or p), with probability .95. If the experimenter specifies B, the desired bound on the error of estimation, then the necessary sample size can be obtained by solving for n in one of two cases.

sample size

1. If the parameter of interest is μ, n is chosen so that

$$2\frac{\sigma}{\sqrt{n}} = B$$

$B^2 ; \dfrac{4\sigma^2}{B^2}$

Solving this equation for n requires squaring both sides of the equation. Then

$$\dfrac{4\sigma^2}{n} = \underline{\hspace{2cm}} \quad \text{and} \quad n = \underline{\hspace{2cm}}$$

2. If the parameter of interest is p, n is chosen so that

$$2\sqrt{\dfrac{pq}{n}} = B$$

then

$4\dfrac{pq}{n} ; \dfrac{4pq}{B^2}$

$$\underline{\hspace{2cm}} = B^2 \quad \text{and} \quad n = \underline{\hspace{2cm}}$$

Example 11.4
Suppose it is known that $\sigma = 2.25$ and it is desired to estimate μ with a bound on the error of estimation less than or equal to .5 unit with probability .95. How large a sample should be taken?

$\bar{y} ; 2\dfrac{\sigma}{\sqrt{n}}$

Solution
The estimator for μ is $\underline{\hspace{2cm}}$ with bound on error $\underline{\hspace{2cm}}$. The experimenter desires this bound to be $B = .5$. Then, using the formula given as $n = 4\sigma^2/B^2$, we have

2.25; .25; 81

$$n = \dfrac{4\sigma^2}{B^2} = \dfrac{4(\underline{\hspace{1.5cm}})^2}{(.5)^2} = \dfrac{4(5.0625)}{\underline{\hspace{1.5cm}}} = \underline{\hspace{1.5cm}}$$

81

The solution is to take a sample of size $\underline{\hspace{2cm}}$ or greater to insure that the bound is less than or equal to .5 unit.

Example 11.5
The general manager of a large firm is interested in estimating the number of overtime hours per week for one of the firm's subsidiaries. It is known that overtime hours per week will range from 10 to 160 hours. If a sampling plan rather than a complete audit were to be used, how many weekly records should be checked to insure that the estimate is no further than 5 hours from the true mean with probability .95?

5

Solution
The bound B is specified as $B = \underline{\hspace{2cm}}$. However, σ is unknown. Using an estimate based on the range (section 3.6 of the study guide), we can approximate σ as

$$\sigma \approx \frac{\text{range}}{4} = \frac{160 - 10}{4} = \frac{\underline{\hspace{2cm}}}{4} = \underline{\hspace{1cm}}$$

150; 37.5

The required sample size is

$$n = \frac{4\sigma^2}{B^2} = \frac{4(\underline{\hspace{2cm}})^2}{(5)^2} = \underline{\hspace{1cm}}$$

37.5; 225

The general manager must sample $n = \underline{\hspace{2cm}}$ weekly records.

225

Example 11.6
If an experimenter wished to estimate the fraction of university students that daily read the college newspaper, correct to within .03 with probability .95, how large a sample of students should she take?

Solution
To estimate the binomial parameter p, the estimator is $\hat{p}$ with bound on error $2\sqrt{pq/n}$. This bound is specified as $B = .03$, so that the required sample size is given in 2, above, as

$$n = \frac{4pq}{B^2} = \frac{4pq}{(.03)^2}$$

Since neither p nor $\hat{p}$ is known, we can solve for n by assuming the worst possible variation, which occurs when $p = q = \underline{\hspace{2cm}}$. Hence,

.5

$$n = \frac{4(.5)(.5)}{(.03)^2} = \frac{1}{.0009} = 1111.1111$$

Therefore, a conservative sample size of $n = 1112$ should be taken to achieve the bound required, even if faced with the maximum possible variation. The student should realize that if a more accurate estimate of p is available, that estimate should be used in place of $p = .5$, providing a (smaller, larger) sample size necessary to achieve the given bound B.

smaller

   This same procedure can be used to find the sample sizes, n_1 and n_2, required to estimate the difference in two population means. The bound on the error of estimation is

$$2\sigma_{\bar{y}_1 - \bar{y}_2} = 2\sqrt{\frac{\sigma_1^2}{n_1} + \frac{\sigma_2^2}{n_2}}$$

Example 11.7
An experiment is to be conducted to compare two different sales techniques at a number of sales centers. Suppose that the range of sales for the sales centers is

expected to be $4000. How many centers should be included for each of the sales techniques in order to estimate the difference in mean sales correct to within $500?

Solution

We will assume that the two sample sizes are equal, that is, $n_1 = n_2 = n$. Then the required common sample size n is found by solving for n in the equation

$$\underline{\hspace{2cm}} = B$$

The quantities σ_1^2 and σ_2^2 are unknown but we know that the range is expected to be $4000. Then we would take $\sigma_1 = \sigma_2 = \underline{\hspace{1.5cm}}$ as the best available approximation. Then, substituting into the equation above,

1000

$2(1000)^2/n$

$$2\sqrt{\underline{\hspace{1.5cm}}} = 500$$

32

or $\qquad n = \underline{\hspace{1.5cm}}$

32

Thus $n = \underline{\hspace{1.5cm}}$ sales centers would be required for each of the two sales techniques.

Self-Correcting Exercises 11B

1. A device is known to produce measurements whose errors in measurement are normally distributed with a standard deviation $\sigma = 8$ millimeters. If the average measurement is to be reported, how many repeated measurements should be used so that the error in measurement is no larger than 3 millimeters with probability .95?
2. How many items from a production line should be sampled to estimate the true proportion of defectives for the line to within .01 with probability .95? The value of p is expected to be at most 0.1.
3. An experiment is being conducted to estimate the average taste threshold level for a particular food additive as measured by its concentration in parts per million. How many subjects should be included in the experimental group in order to estimate the mean threshold level to within 10 units if the range of the measurements is expected to be approximately 80 parts per million?
4. How many individuals from a politically oriented group should be included in a poll designed to estimate the true proportion favoring a tuition increase at the state university correct to within .01 with probability .95? (In the absence of any prior information regarding the value of p, solve the problem assuming maximum variation.)

EXERCISES

1. List two factors that affect the quantity of information in an experiment.
2. A doctor wishes to estimate the average nicotine content in a certain brand of cigarettes correct to within .5 milligram. From previous experiments it is known that σ is in the neighborhood of 4 milligrams. How large a sample should the doctor take to be 95% confident of her estimate?
3. A manufacturer of dresses believes that approximately 20% of his product contains flaws. If he wishes to estimate the true percentage to within 8%, how large a sample should he take?
4. It is desired to estimate $(\mu_1 - \mu_2)$ from information contained in independent random samples from populations with variances $\sigma_1^2 = 9$ and $\sigma_2^2 = 16$. If the two sample sizes are to be equal $(n_1 = n_2 = n)$, how large should n be in order to estimate $(\mu_1 - \mu_2)$ with an error less than 1.0 (with probability equal to .95)?
5. To test the comparative brightness of two red dyes, nine samples of cloth were taken from a production line and each sample was divided into two pieces. One of the two pieces in each sample was randomly chosen and red dye 1 applied; red dye 2 was applied to the remaining piece. The following data represent a "brightness score" for each piece. Is there sufficient evidence to indicate a difference in mean brightness scores for the two dyes? (Use $\alpha = .01$.)

Sample	Dye 1	Dye 2
1	10	8
2	12	11
3	9	10
4	8	6
5	15	12
6	12	13
7	9	9
8	10	8
9	15	13

6. Refer to exercise 5. Find a 99% confidence interval for $(\mu_1 - \mu_2)$, the difference in mean brightness scores for the two dyes.
7. If a mental health agency would like to estimate the percentage of local clinic patients that are referred to their counseling center to within 5 percentage points with 95% accuracy, how many patient records should be sampled?
8. To test the effect of alcohol in increasing the reaction time to respond to a given stimulus, the reaction times of seven persons were measured. After each had consumed 3 ounces of 40% alcohol, the reaction time for each of the seven persons was measured again. Do the following data indicate that the mean reaction time after consuming alcohol was greater than the mean reaction time before consuming alcohol? (Use $\alpha = .05$.)

Person	Before (time in seconds)	After (time in seconds)
1	4	7
2	5	8
3	5	3
4	4	5
5	3	4
6	6	5
7	2	5

9. It is thought that about one-tenth of the individuals in a given population have a certain genetic defect. In order to determine the true fraction with a maximum error of .003 with probability .95, the sample size should be at least how large?

10. In order to bid competitively for the lumbering rights on a certain tract of land, a company needs to know the mean diameter of the trees on the tract to within 2.5 inches. If the company can assume $\sigma = 8$ inches, how large a sample of trees on this tract should be taken?

11. Twenty students are given an attitude test before and after viewing a motion picture designed to change their attitudes favorably toward a new curriculum. A high score indicates a favorable attitude and a low score an unfavorable attitude. (The scores could range from 1 to 30.) From the data given below can we conclude that the motion picture was successful in changing attitudes? (Use $\alpha = .05$.)

Student	Before	After	Student	Before	After
1	15	20	11	19	22
2	20	21	12	14	13
3	17	16	13	8	13
4	6	5	14	11	15
5	12	19	15	24	25
6	14	17	16	19	20
7	20	23	17	16	22
8	15	14	18	22	20
9	19	17	19	15	18
10	26	25	20	21	28

Chapter   12

TESTING THE EQUALITY
OF POPULATION VARIANCES

12.1 Introduction

In many cases the measure of variability is more important than that of central tendency. For example, an educational test consisting of 100 items has a mean score of 75 with standard deviation of 2.5. The value $\mu = 75$ may sound impressive, but $\sigma = 2.5$ would imply that this test has very poor discriminating ability since approximately 95% of the scores would be between 70 and 80. In like manner, a production line producing bearings with $\mu = .5$ inch and $\sigma = .2$ inch would produce many defective items; the fact that the bearings have a mean diameter of .5 inch would be of little value when the bearings are fitted together. *The precision of an instrument, whether it be an educational test or a machine, is measured by the standard deviation of the error of measurement.* Hence, it is sometimes necessary to make inferences concerning population variation as well as to make inferences concerning population means.

Inference concerning population variation can take the form of _____ or _____ _____ for a single population variance, σ^2, for comparing two population variances σ_1^2 and σ_2^2, or for comparing more than two population variances. In this text, we will discuss only one specific type of inference; in particular, we will test the hypothesis $H_0: \sigma_1^2 = \sigma_2^2$ where σ_1^2 and σ_2^2 are the variances of two normal populations. There are several reasons for this:

    estimation
    hypothesis testing

1. An experimenter may have some specific need for the test. For example, he may wish to compare the variability of two testing procedures or compare the precision of one manufacturing process with another.
2. One may wish to compare two population variances prior to using a t test to make sure that the assumption of equal variances is not being violated.
3. The comparison of two sources of variation is inherent in a method of

analysis used for comparing several population means. This *analysis of variance* is introduced in chapter 13.

12.2 A Test of an Hypothesis Concerning Two Population Variances

To test the hypothesis of equality of two population variances,

$$H_0: \ \sigma_1^2 = \sigma_2^2$$

we need to make the following assumptions:

normal
1. Each population sampled has a _____ distribution.

independent
2. The samples are _____.

The statistic s_1^2/s_2^2 is used to test

$$H_0: \ \sigma_1^2 = \sigma_2^2$$

against a one- or two-tailed alternative of the form

1. $\qquad H_a: \ \sigma_1^2 \neq \sigma_2^2$

2. $\qquad H_a: \ \sigma_1^2 > \sigma_2^2$

3. $\qquad H_a: \ \sigma_1^2 < \sigma_2^2$

large
small
A _____ value of this statistic implies that $\sigma_1^2 > \sigma_2^2$; a _____ value of this statistic implies that $\sigma_1^2 < \sigma_2^2$; while a value of the statistic close to one (1) implies that $\sigma_1^2 = \sigma_2^2$. In repeated sampling this statistic has an F distribution when $\sigma_1^2 = \sigma_2^2$ with the following properties:

nonsymmetric
1. The distribution of F is (symmetric, nonsymmetric).
2. The shape of the distribution depends on the degrees of freedom, $v_1 = n_1 - 1$ and $v_2 = n_2 - 1$.

zero
3. F is always greater than or equal to _____. The tabulation of critical values of F is complicated by the fact that the distribution is nonsymmetric and must be indexed according to the values of v_1 and v_2, the degrees of freedom associated with the numerator and denominator of the F statistic. As we will see, however, it will be sufficient to have only right-tailed critical values of F for the various combinations of v_1 and v_2. Tables 4 and 5 in the text have tabulated right-tailed critical values for the F statistic, where F_a is

that value of F having an area of a to its right, based on v_1 and v_2, the degrees of freedom associated with the *numerator* and *denominator* of F, respectively. F_a satisfies the relationship $P(F > F_a) = a$.

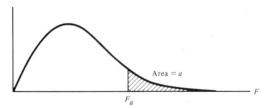

Area = a

F_a

Table 4 has values of F_a for $a = .05$ and various values of v_1 and v_2 between 1 and ∞, while Table 5 has the same information for $a = .01$.

Example 12.1

Find the value of F based on $v_1 = 5$ and $v_2 = 7$ degrees of freedom such that

$$P(F > F_{.05}) = .05$$

Solution

1. We wish to find a critical value of F with an area $a = .05$ to its right based on $v_1 = 5$ and $v_2 = 7$ degrees of freedom. Therefore, we will use Table 4.
2. Values of v_1 are found along the *top* margin of the table while values of v_2 appear on both the right *and* left margins of the table. Find the value of $v_1 = 5$ along the top margin and cross-index this value with $v_2 = 7$ along the left margin to find $F_{.05} = 3.97$.

Example 12.2

Find the critical right-tailed values of F for the following:

	v_1	v_2	a	F_a	
a.	5	2	.05	_____	19.30
b.	7	15	.05	_____	2.71
c.	20	10	.01	_____	4.41
d.	30	40	.05	_____	1.74
e.	17	13	.01	_____	3.76

We can always avoid using left-tailed critical values of the F distribution by using the following approach. In testing $H_0: \sigma_1^2 \; \sigma_2^2$ against the alternative $H_a: \sigma_1^2 > \sigma_2^2$, we would reject H_0 only if s_1^2/s_2^2 is too large (larger than a right-tailed critical value of F). In testing $H_0: \sigma_1^2 = \sigma_2^2$ against $H_a: \sigma_1^2 < \sigma_2^2$, we would reject H_0 only if s_2^2/s_1^2 were too large. In testing $H_0: \sigma_1^2 = \sigma_2^2$ against the two-tailed alternative $H_a: \sigma_1^2 \neq \sigma_2^2$, we will agree to *designate the population that produced the larger sample variance as population 1 and the larger sample variance as s_1^2*. We then agree to reject H_0 if s_1^2/s_2^2 is *too large*.

When we agree to designate the population with the larger sample variance as population 1, the test of $H_0: \sigma_1^2 = \sigma_2^2$ versus $H_a: \sigma_1^2 \neq \sigma_2^2$ using s_1^2/s_2^2 will be right-tailed. However, in so doing we must remember that the tabulated tail area must be doubled to get the actual significance level of the test. For example, if the critical right-tailed value of F has been found from Table 4 the actual significance level of the test will be $\alpha = 2(.05) = $ _____ . If the critical value comes from Table 5, the actual level will be $\alpha = 2(.01) = $ _____ .

.10
.02

Example 12.3

An experimenter has performed a laboratory experiment using two groups of rats. One group was given a standard treatment while the second received a newly developed treatment. Wishing to test the hypothesis $H_0: \mu_1 = \mu_2$, the experimenter suspects that the population variances are not equal, an assumption necessary for using the t statistic in testing the equality of the means. Use the following data to test if the experimenter's suspicion is warranted at the $\alpha = .02$ level:

	Old Treatment	New Treatment
	$s = 2.3$	$s = 5.8$
	$n = 10$	$n = 10$

Solution

This problem involves a test of the equality of two population variances. Let population 1 be the population receiving the new treatment.

1. $H_0: \sigma_1^2 = \sigma_2^2$

2. $H_a: \sigma_1^2 \neq \sigma_2^2$

3. Test statistic:

$$F = s_1^2/s_2^2$$

4. Rejection region: With $\nu_1 = \nu_2 = 9$ degrees of freedom, reject H_0 if $F > F_{.01}$

5.35

$= $ _____ .

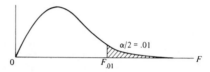

Now we calculate the test statistic.

$$F = \frac{s_1^2}{s_2^2}$$

$$= \frac{(5.8)^2}{(2.3)^2}$$

$$= \frac{(\underline{\hspace{1cm}})}{(\underline{\hspace{1cm}})}$$ 33.64;
                                                                        5.29

$$= \underline{\hspace{1cm}}$$ 6.36

5. Decision: Since F is (greater, less) than $F_{.01} = 5.35$, $H_0: \sigma_1^2 = \sigma_2^2$ (is, is not)   greater; is
   rejected.

   Since the population variances were judged to be different, the experimenter
   is not justified in using the t statistic to test $H_0: \mu_1 - \mu_2 = 0$. She must resort to other methods, several of which will be discussed in chapter 15.

Example 12.4
A comparison of the precisions of two machines developed for extracting juice
from oranges is to be made using the following data:

Machine A	Machine B
$s^2 = 3.1$ ounces^2	$s^2 = 1.4$ ounces^2
$n = 25$	$n = 25$

Is there sufficient evidence to indicate that $\sigma_A^2 > \sigma_B^2$ at the $\alpha = .05$ level?

Solution
Let population 1 be the population of measurements on machine A. The test
would proceed as follows:

1. $H_0: \sigma_1^2 = \sigma_2^2$

2. $H_a: \sigma_1^2 \underline{\hspace{1cm}} \sigma_2^2$ $>$

3. Test statistic:

   $$F = \frac{s_1^2}{s_2^2}$$

4. Rejection region: Based on $v_1 = v_2 = \underline{\hspace{1cm}}$ degrees of freedom, we will   24
   reject H_0 if $F > F_{.05}$ with $F_{.05} = \underline{\hspace{1cm}}$.   1.98

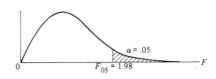

The value of the statistic is

$$F = \frac{s_1^2}{s_2^2}$$

2.21

$$= \frac{3.1}{1.4} = \underline{\hspace{2cm}}$$

is

5. Decision: We reject H_0 and conclude that the variability of machine A (is, is not) greater than that of machine B.

EXERCISES

1. Refer to exercise 9, chapter 9. In using the t statistic in testing an hypothesis concerning $(\mu_1 - \mu_2)$, one assumes that $\sigma_1^2 = \sigma_2^2$. Based on the sample information, could you conclude that this assumption had been met for this problem?

2. An experiment to explore the pain thresholds to electrical shock for males and females resulted in the following data summary:

	Males	Females
n	10	13
$\bar{y}$	15.1	12.6
s^2	11.3	26.9

Do these data supply sufficient evidence to indicate a significant difference in variability of thresholds for these two groups at the 10% level of significance?

3. Find the critical right-tailed values of F for the following:

	ν_1	ν_2	a
a.	9	13	.01
b.	1	8	.01
c.	6	5	.05
d.	6	15	.01
e.	30	30	.05

4. In a test of heat resistance involving two types of metal paint, two groups of 10 metal strips were randomly formed. Group one was painted with type I paint, while group two was painted with type II paint. The metal strips were placed in an oven in random order, heated, and the temperature at which the paint began to crack and peel recorded for each strip. Do the following data indicate that the variability in the critical temperatures differs for the two types of paint? (Use $\alpha = .10$.)

	$\bar{y}$	s^2	n
Type I	$280.1°F$	93.2	10
Type II	$269.9°F$	51.9	10

5. In an attempt to reduce the variability of machine parts produced by process A, a manufacturer has introduced process B (a modification of A). Do the following data, based on two samples of 25 items, indicate that the manufacturer has achieved his goal? (Use $\alpha = .05$.)

	n	s^2
Process A	25.	6.57
Process B	25	3.19

6. Two different examinations are being considered for use as a perceptual motor ability test. It is desired to find out if one test is better designed to ascertain differences among first graders. Twenty first graders take both exams with the following results. The average on both tests was approximately 12, but $s_1^2 = 4.5$ and $s_2^2 = 2.3$. Do the data indicate a difference in variability of the two tests? (Use $\alpha = .10$.)

7. Two different machines are available to measure the results of an experiment. Machine I is now in position to use, and Machine II would be used only if $\sigma_1^2 > \sigma_2^2$. The following measurements were obtained from each machine.

Machine I	Machine II
0.3	0.8
1.4	1.6
1.2	1.2
0.7	0.9
0.4	0.7
	0.9

Do the data indicate that $\sigma_1^2 > \sigma_2^2$? Test at the 5% level of significance.

Chapter 13
ANALYSIS OF VARIANCE

13.1 Introduction

Chapters 8 and 9 were concerned with methods of inference for comparing two population means. In many situations, however, the experimenter is really in-terested in a comparison of more than two means. For example, the researcher in example 8.1, who was interested in the effect of vitamin C on average choles-terol level, might be interested in comparing average cholesterol levels for sev-eral different doses of vitamin C. The experimenter in example 8.3 might be interested in comparing the mean absorption rates for several different drugs. In this chapter, we will present a technique that allows a test of the equality of more than two means. The technique, which can also be used in analyzing sev-eral more complicated experimental designs, is called the *analysis of variance*.

13.2 The Logic Behind an Analysis of Variance

In this chapter, we assume that k independent random samples, not necessarily the same size, have been drawn from k normal populations, all of which have the same common variance, σ^2. The objective will be to determine whether or not the population means are equal; that is, we would like to test the null hypothesis

$$H_0: \quad \mu_1 = \mu_2 = \mu_3 = \ldots = \mu_k$$

against the alternative

$$H_a: \quad \text{at least one mean is different}$$

Let us consider these two hypotheses portrayed graphically:

1. If H_0 is true, then all k samples are being drawn from a common normal population with mean μ and variance σ^2.

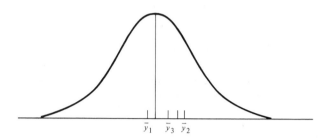

$\bar{y}_1 \quad \bar{y}_3 \; \bar{y}_2$

Hence, measurements from the various samples with common sample size n should be randomly scattered along the horizontal axis. The variation within any one sample will estimate _____, as will a pooled estimate of the variation within all k samples. The variation between the sample means will be smaller than the overall variation. Recall from chapter 5 that the variance of a sample mean drawn from a population with mean μ and variance σ^2 is

$$\sigma_{\bar{y}}^2 = \underline{\hspace{3cm}}$$

Hence, the variation between the k sample means should estimate σ^2/n. If we compare the variation within k samples with _____ times the variation between the k sample means, they should be approximately the same.

2. If H_a is true, and in fact all the means are different, then the k samples are being drawn from different normal populations with a common variance σ^2. When the population means are different, the measurements from the various samples will no longer be scattered along the horizontal axis.

Suppose that we have sampled from four populations having different means as shown in the following figure.

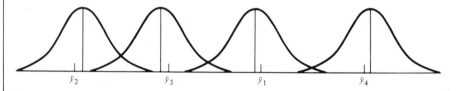

$\bar{y}_2 \qquad\qquad \bar{y}_3 \qquad\qquad \bar{y}_1 \qquad\qquad \bar{y}_4$

Most of the measurements from sample 2 will be clustered to the left, while measurements from sample 4 will be clustered to the right. Some mixing or overlapping of the measurements may occur within the intervals where the curves overlap; however, there will be a wider variation in the measurements. The variation within any one sample will still estimate σ^2, the common population

σ^2

$\dfrac{\sigma^2}{n}$

n

variance, as will a pooled estimate of the variation within all k samples. However, the variation between the sample means will be (smaller, larger) than σ^2/n,
since the sample means *are not* being drawn from the same population. If we
compare the variation within samples to n times the variation between sample
means, the variation between samples will be (smaller, larger) than the variation
within samples.

larger

larger

If the variation between the sample means is large when compared to the variation within the samples, there is evidence to indicate that a difference exists
between the means of the populations from which the samples were drawn.

13.3 A Test of an Hypothesis Concerning More than Two Population Means: An Example of an Analysis of Variance

In order to formalize the procedure discussed in section 13.2 for testing whether
or not there is evidence of a difference between population means, let us consider the following example.

Example 13.1
Five different subjects were observed under each of three treatment conditions.
The following observations were recorded:

	Condition 1	*Condition 2*	*Condition 3*
	25	32	36
	33	43	31
	42	38	40
	27	47	28
	36	30	45
Sum	163	190	180
	$\bar{y}_1 = $ _____	$\bar{y}_2 = $ _____	$\bar{y}_3 = $ _____
	$s_1^2 = 47.3$	$s_2^2 = 51.5$	$s_3^2 = 46.5$

32.6; 38; 36

It is of interest to the experimenter to know if a difference in the means exists
for the three conditions.

Recall in chapter 9 that we tested the difference in two population means using the test statistic

$$t = \frac{(\bar{y}_1 - \bar{y}_2)}{\sqrt{s^2 \left(\frac{1}{n_1} + \frac{1}{n_2}\right)}} \quad \text{where} \quad s^2 = \frac{(n_1 - 1)s_1^2 + (n_2 - 1)s_2^2}{n_1 + n_2 - 2}$$

The test that will be presented here is in fact an extension of this test statistic,
allowing us to compare k sample means simultaneously.

The variation within sample measurements from the same population is measured by the sample variance. For the data corresponding to condition one in example 13.1

$$s_1^2 = \frac{1}{(5-1)} \Sigma(y_1 - \bar{y}_1)^2$$

The sample variances for conditions 2 and 3 are calculated in an analogous manner. The estimate of the total within-sample variation is simply the pooled estimate of the sample variances from the individual samples:

$$s_W^2 = \frac{(n_1 - 1)s_1^2 + (n_2 - 1)s_2^2 + (n_3 - 1)s_3^2}{(n_1 - 1) + (n_2 - 1) + (n_3 - 1)}$$

s_W^2 provides an estimate of σ^2, the common variance of all k populations. For our example,

51.5; 5

$$s_W^2 = \frac{(5-1)(47.3) + (5-1)(\underline{\hspace{1cm}}) + (\underline{\hspace{1cm}} - 1)(46.5)}{(5-1) + (5-1) + (5-1)}$$

12

$$= \frac{581.2}{(\underline{\hspace{1cm}})}$$

48.43

$$= \underline{\hspace{1cm}}$$

Since $(n-1)s^2 = \Sigma(y - \bar{y})^2$ for each sample, an equivalent formula for s_W^2 is

$$s_W^2 = \frac{\Sigma(y_1 - \bar{y}_1)^2 + \Sigma(y_2 - \bar{y}_2)^2 + \Sigma(y_3 - \bar{y}_3)^2}{n_1 + n_2 + n_3 - 3}$$

When the sample sizes are all equal, the variance of the three sample means, $s_{\bar{y}}^2$, is calculated as

$$s_{\bar{y}}^2 = \frac{\Sigma\bar{y}^2 - \frac{(\Sigma\bar{y})^2}{3}}{3 - 1}$$

106.6

$$= \frac{32.6^2 + 38^2 + 36^2 - \frac{(\underline{\hspace{1cm}})^2}{3}}{2}$$

$$= \frac{\underline{\hspace{2cm}} - 3787.8533}{2}$$

| | 3802.76 |

$$= \underline{\hspace{2cm}}$$

| | 7.4533 |

The distribution of sample means of size $n = 5$ has variance $\sigma^2/n = \sigma^2/5$. If H_0 is true, a second estimate of σ^2 is then

$$s_B^2 = ns_{\bar{y}}^2 = 5(\underline{\hspace{2cm}}) = \underline{\hspace{2cm}}$$

| | 7.4533; 37.2667 |

If s_B^2 is substantially larger than s_W^2, the truth of H_0 will be in doubt.
It can be shown that, if H_0 is true, the test statistic

$$F = \frac{s_B^2}{s_W^2}$$

has an F distribution with degrees of freedom corresponding to the two sample variances. That is,

$$\nu_1 = k - 1 = \underline{\hspace{2cm}}$$

| | 2 |

and $\nu_2 = 3n - 3 = \underline{\hspace{2cm}} - 3 = \underline{\hspace{2cm}}.$

| | 15; 12 |

If the population means are different, s_B^2 will be (smaller, larger) than expected.
Thus, we should reject H_0 if the calculated value of F falls in a(n) (upper, lower)-tailed rejection region.

| | larger |
| | upper |

For example 13.1, using $\alpha = .05$, the rejection region is found by indexing $\nu_1 = 2$ and $\nu_2 = 12$ in Table 4. The null hypothesis will be rejected if

$$F > F_{.05} = \underline{\hspace{2cm}}$$

| | 3.89 |

Calculating the observed value of the test statistic,

$$F = \frac{s_B^2}{s_W^2} = \frac{37.2667}{48.43} = \underline{\hspace{2cm}}$$

| | .77 |

The null hypothesis is not rejected and we cannot conclude that a difference exists between the three population means.

General Test of the Difference in k Population Means

The test presented using example 13.1 was presented using equal samples of size n, so that the logic behind the F test would be clear. The test can be generalized however to account for unequal samples of sizes $n_1, n_2, \ldots, n_k$. The four parts of this statistical test are given below.

1.　　　$H_0: \mu_1 = \mu_2 = \mu_3 = \ldots = \mu_k$

2.　　　H_a: at least one mean is different

3. Test statistic:

$$F = \frac{s_B^2}{s_W^2}$$

where

$$s_B^2 = \frac{\Sigma n_i \bar{y}_i^2 - \dfrac{(\Sigma n_i \bar{y}_i)^2}{n'}}{k - 1}$$

$$s_W^2 = \frac{(n_1 - 1)s_1^2 + \ldots + (n_k - 1)s_k^2}{n_1 + n_2 + \ldots + n_k - k}$$

$$n' = n_1 + n_2 + \ldots + n_k$$

4. Rejection region: With $\nu_1 = k - 1$ and $\nu_2 = n_1 + n_2 + \ldots + n_k - k$, reject H_0 if F exceeds a critical value found in Table 4 or 5 with area $\alpha = .05$ or $\alpha = .01$ to its right.

Note that when $n_1 = n_2 = \ldots = n_k = n$, s_B^2 reduces to the formula given earlier in the section:

$$s_B^2 = n \left(\frac{\Sigma \bar{y}^2 - \dfrac{(\Sigma \bar{y})^2}{k}}{k - 1} \right)$$

Example 13.2

Do the following data provide sufficient evidence to indicate a difference in the means of the three underlying treatment populations?

	Treatment		
	1	*2*	*3*
	3	7	5
	4	9	4
	2	8	5
		7	
$\bar{y}_i$	_____	_____	_____
n_i	3	4	3
s_i^2	1.00	_____	.3333

3; 7.75; 4.6667

.9167

Solution

1. Calculate

$$s_W^2 = \frac{(n_1 - 1)s_1^2 + (n_2 - 1)s_2^2 + (n_3 - 1)s_3^2}{n_1 + n_2 + n_3 - 3}$$

$$= \frac{2(1.00) + 3(\underline{}) + 2(.3333)}{10 - 3}$$ .9167

$$= \frac{2 + \underline{} + .6667}{7}$$ 2.75

$$= \underline{}$$ .77

$$s_B^2 = \frac{\Sigma n_i \bar{y}_i^2 - \frac{(\Sigma n_i \bar{y}_i)^2}{n'}}{k - 1}$$

$$= \frac{3(3^2) + 4(7.75^2) + 3(4.6667^2) - (\underline{})^2/10}{2}$$ 9 + 31 + 14

$$= \frac{\underline{} - 291.6}{2}$$ 332.5843

$$= \underline{}$$ 20.49

2. The test statistic to test the null hypothesis $H_0: \mu_1 = \mu_2 = \mu_3$ is

$$F = \frac{s_B^2}{s_W^2} = \frac{20.49}{.77} = \underline{}$$ 26.61

which has an F distribution with $v_1 = \underline{}$ and $v_2 = \underline{}$ 2; 7
degrees of freedom.

3. Rejection region: With $\alpha = .05$, we shall reject H_0 if $F > F_{.05} = \underline{}$. 4.74

4. $F = \underline{}$ is (greater, less) than $F_{.05} = 4.74$. Hence, we (reject, do not 26.61; greater; reject
reject) H_0 and conclude that there is evidence to indicate a difference in
means for the three treatment populations at the $\alpha = .05$ level of significance.

Example 13.3

In the investigation of a citizens committee's complaint about the availability of
fire protection within the county, the distance in miles to the nearest fire sta-
tion was measured for each of 5 randomly selected residences in each of four
areas.

	Areas			
	1	*2*	*3*	*4*
	7	1	7	4
	5	4	9	6
	5	3	8	3
	6	4	7	7
	8	5	8	5
$\bar{y}_i$	_____	3.4	_____	5.0
n_i	5	5	5	5
s_i^2	1.7	_____	0.7	_____

6.2; 7.8 (margin, next to $\bar{y}_i$)

2.3; 2.5 (margin, next to s_i^2)

Do these data provide sufficient evidence to indicate a difference in mean distance for the four areas at the $\alpha = .01$ level of significance?

Solution

1. Calculate

$$s_W^2 = \frac{(n_1 - 1)s_1^2 + (n_2 - 1)s_2^2 + (n_3 - 1)s_3^2 + (n_4 - 1)s_4^2}{n_1 + n_2 + n_3 + n_4 - 4}$$

$$= \frac{4(1.7 + 2.3 + 0.7 + 2.5)}{16}$$

7.2; 1.8 (margin)

$$= \frac{\overline{}}{4} = \overline{}$$

Since the four samples are of equal size with $n = 5$, the formula for s_B^2 reduces to

$$s_B^2 = n\left(\frac{\Sigma \bar{y}^2 - (\Sigma \bar{y})^2/4}{3}\right)$$

5; 22.4 (margin)

$$= \overline{}\left(\frac{135.84 - (\underline{})^2/4}{3}\right)$$

125.44 (margin)

$$= \frac{5}{3}(135.84 - \underline{})$$

17.3333 (margin)

$$= \overline{}$$

2. Test of the null hypothesis:

a. $H_0: \mu_1 = \mu_2 = \mu_3 = \mu_4$.

   H_a: At least one equality does not hold.

b. Test statistic:

$$F = \frac{s_B^2}{s_W^2}$$

   with $\nu_1 = $ _____ and $\nu_2 = $ _____ degrees of freedom.   3; 16
c. Rejection region: Reject H_0 if $F > F_{.01} = $ _____.   5.29
d. For these data,

$$F = \frac{17.33}{1.80} = \underline{\hspace{2cm}}$$ 9.63

   Hence, we _____ H_0 and conclude that there is sufficient evidence   reject
   to indicate a difference in mean distance for the four areas.

Self-Correcting Exercises 13A

1. The length of time required for kindergarten-age children to assemble a device
   was compared for four different lengths of preexperiment instructional times.
   Four students were randomly assigned to each group but two were eliminated
   during the experiment due to sickness. The data (assembly times in minutes)
   are shown below:

| | Preexperiment Instructional Time (hours) | | | |
	.5	1.0	1.5	2.0
	8	9	4	4
	14	7	6	7
	9	5	7	5
	12		8	
$\bar{y}_i$	10.75	7.00	6.25	5.33
n_i	4	3	4	3

   Do the data present sufficient evidence to indicate a difference in mean time
   to assemble the device for the four different lengths of instructional time?
   (Use $\alpha = .01$.)
2. In the evaluation of three rations fed to chickens grown for market, the
   dressed weights of five chickens fed from birth on one of the three rations
   were recorded.

		Rations	
	1	2	3
	7.1	4.9	6.7
	6.2	6.6	6.0
	7.0	6.8	7.3
	5.6	4.6	6.2
	6.4	5.3	7.1
n_i	5	5	5
$\bar{y}_i$	6.46	5.64	6.66

Do the data present sufficient evidence to indicate a difference in the mean growth for the three rations as measured by the dressed weights? (Use $\alpha =$ .05.)

13.4 Summary

The test of the equality of several population means presented in this chapter is one of the simplest examples of a technique called an *analysis of variance*. The experimental design for this test is often called a *completely randomized design* and requires that random samples of size $n_1, n_2, \ldots, n_k$ be drawn independently from each of the k populations. The variation between samples is then compared with the variation within samples to determine whether or not a difference in population means is likely. Several comments might be made:
1. It is necessary that each random sample be drawn from a normal population and that all populations have the same common variance σ^2.
2. If the null hypothesis is rejected, we cannot specify which of the k means are different. This requires a series of individual t tests with properly adjusted error rates, or other appropriate methods for comparing the means two at a time.
3. Computer programs can often be used to perform an analysis of variance with minimum time and effort.

Although it is never known in practice whether the assumptions given in 1 are satisfied, we should be reasonably sure that violations of these assumptions are moderate. If the random variable under investigation is discrete, it is possible that the distribution for y is mound-shaped and hence approximately normal. This would not be the case if the discrete random variable only assumed three or four values.

Even when the response is normally distributed, the variances for the treatment groups may still be unequal. In agricultural variety trials it is not unusual for the variability in height of a plant to increase with the average height. Similarly, in economic studies the variability of income within economic groupings is known to increase as the average income increases.

When the data fail to meet the assumptions of normality and equal variances, an appropriate transformation of the data, such as their square roots, logarithms, or some other function of the data values, may be used in order that the transformed values approximately satisfy these assumptions.

When the data consist only of rankings or ordered preferences, appropriate nonparametric testing and estimation procedures can be used. These procedures can also be used when the data fail to satisfy the assumptions of normality and equal variances, since the only requirement needed to use nonparametric techniques is that the observations be _____ within the constraints of the design used.

independent

EXERCISES

1. A large piece of cotton fabric was cut into 12 pieces and randomly partitioned into three groups of four. Three different chemicals designed to produce resistance to stain were applied to the units, one chemical for each group. A stain was applied (as uniformly as possible) over all $n = 12$ units and the intensity of the stain measured in terms of light reflection.

	Chemical	
1	2	3
12	14	9
8	9	7
9	11	9
6	10	5

Do the data present sufficient evidence to indicate a difference in mean resistance to stain for the three chemicals? (Use $\alpha = .05$.)

2. The Graduate Record Examination scores were recorded for students admitted to three different graduate programs in a university.

	Graduate Programs	
1	2	3
532	670	502
601	590	607
548	640	549
619	710	524
509		542
627		
690		

Do these data provide sufficient evidence to indicate a difference in mean level of achievement on the GRE for applicants admitted to the three programs? (Use $\alpha = .01$.)

3. Twenty maladjusted children were randomly separated into four equal

groups and subjected to 3 months of psychological treatment. A slightly different technique was employed for each group. At the end of the 3-month period, progress was measured by a psychological test. The scores are shown below (one child in group 3 dropped out of the experiment).

	Group				
	1	*2*	*3*	*4*	
	112	111	140	101	
	92	129	121	116	
	124	102	130	105	
	89	136	106	126	
	97	99		119	
Total	514	577	497	567	2155

Do the data present sufficient evidence to indicate a difference in mean response on the test for the four techniques? (Use $\alpha = .05$.)

4. An experiment is going to be run to investigate exploratory activity in relation to environmental history. From a colony of inbred mice, 10 are chosen at random. After weaning, 5 mice are randomly chosen and placed in a large cage containing many stimulating toys and are reared together. The other 5 mice are isolated in individual cages. After 6 weeks, the animals are placed in a strange environment for one hour. The number of minutes spent exploring are shown below:

Group reared mice	Isolated mice
43	15
32	25
48	22
41	38
37	27

Do the data provide sufficient evidence to indicate a difference in the mean time spent exploring for the two groups? (Use $\alpha = .05$.)
   a. Use the t test given in chapter 9.
   b. Use the F test for $k = 2$.
   c. What is the relationship between t and F in this situation?

5. In a learning experiment involving laboratory animals, 15 animals were randomly divided into three groups of 5 animals. The groups were assigned to use one of three methods, each of which involved a different incentive-reward combination. The number of trials required to achieve a predetermined criterion was measured for each animal. The data follow.

	Method	
1	*2*	*3*
20	10	26
25	12	24
17	13	23
13	16	19
19	14	23

Is there a difference in mean number of trials for the three methods? (Use α = .05.)

6. Fifteen subjects with relatively equal reaction times and physical attributes were randomly grouped in fives. The first five were to react to a light stimulus, the second five to a sound stimulus, the third five to stimulus of both sound and light. The results are shown below.

Light	*Sound*	*Both*
.36	.49	.29
.41	.42	.37
.45	.35	.42
.42	.48	.41
.31	.40	.47

Is there sufficient evidence to indicate a difference in reaction times for the 3 stimuli? (Use α = .05.)

Chapter   14

CONTINGENCY TABLES

14.1 Introduction

Examine the following experimental situations for any general similarities:
1. Two hundred people are classified according to their blood type and the number of people in each blood type group is recorded.
2. A sample of 100 items is randomly selected from a production line. Each item is classified as belonging to one of three groups: acceptables, seconds, or rejects. The number in each group is recorded.
3. A random sample of 50 books is taken from the local library. Each book is assigned to one of three categories: science, art, or fiction. The number of books in each category is recorded.

Each of these situations is similar to the others in that classes or categories are defined and the number of items falling into each category is recorded. Hence these experiments result in enumerative or _____ data. A statistic that allows us to make inferences about situations involving count or enumerative data was developed by the British statistician Karl Pearson around 1900. We will use Pearson's statistic to investigate the dependence or independence between two methods of classification.

count

14.2 Contingency Tables: A Test for Determining Whether Two Methods of Classification Are Independent

If we were to classify people first according to their hair color and second according to their complexion, would these methods of classification be independent of each other? We might classify students first according to the college in which they are enrolled and second according to their grade-point average. Would these two methds of classification be independent? In each problem we

contingency

are asking if one method of classification is *contingent* on another. We investigate this problem by displaying our data according to the two methods of classification in an array called a _____ table.

Example 14.1

A criminologist studying criminal offenders who have a record of one or more arrests is interested in knowing if the educational achievement level of the offender influences the frequency of arrests. He has classified his data using four educational achievement level classifications:

        A: completed 6th grade or less
        B: completed 7th, 8th or 9th grade
        C: completed 10th, 11th, or 12th grade
        D: education beyond 12th grade

Number of Arrests	*Educational Achievement*				*Total*
	A	*B*	*C*	*D*	
1	55	40	43	30	168
2	15	25	18	22	80
3 or more	7	8	12	10	37
Total	77	73	73	62	285

independent

does not

The null hypothesis of interest is that the two methods of classification are (independent, dependent). That is, the educational achievement level of the offender (does, does not) influence the frequency of arrests. The alternative hypothesis is that the two methods of classification are dependent.

   Pearson's statistic (given below) utilizes the squares of the deviations of the observed from the expected number of observations falling in each cell, under the assumption that H_0 is true:

$$X^2 = \Sigma \frac{(O - E)^2}{E}$$

cell

where O is the observed cell count and E is the expected cell count for a particular cell. For example 14.1, the expected cell frequencies or counts are defined to be the number of offenders we would expect to observe in each category or _____ if in fact the null hypothesis of independence is true. We will discuss a method for obtaining estimates of E later in this section. The calculation $(O - E)^2/E$ is made for each cell, and the sum is taken over all cells.

   Note that the deviations are divided by the expected number so that the deviations are weighted according to whether the expected number is large or small.

1.25

A deviation of 5 from an expected number of 20 contributes $(5)^2/20 =$ _____ to X^2, while a deviation of 5 from an expected number of 10 contributes $(5)^2/$

2.50

$10 =$ _____, or *twice* as much, to X^2.

When n, the number of trials, is large, this statistic has an approximate χ^2 distribution, provided the expected numbers in each cell are not too small. We will require as a rule of thumb that $E \geqslant$ _____ . This requirement can be satisfied by combining those cells with small expected numbers until every cell has an expected number of at least _____ . For small deviations from the expected cell counts, the value of the statistic would be (large, small), supporting the hypothesized cell probabilities. However, for large deviations from the expected counts, the value of the statistic would be (large, small), and the hypothesized values of the cell probabilities would be _____ . Hence a one-tailed test is used, rejecting H_0 when X^2 is _____ .

The Chi-square distribution has not been encountered so far in our discussions. It has the following properties:

1. The distribution of χ^2 is (symmetric, nonsymmetric).
2. $\chi^2 \geqslant$ _____ .
3. The distribution of χ^2, like that of t, depends on the degrees of freedom. Since χ^2 does not have a symmetric distribution, critical values of χ^2 have been tabulated for both the upper and lower tails of the distribution in Table 3 of the text. The degrees of freedom are listed along both the right and left margins of the table. Across the top margin are values of χ_a^2, indicating a value of χ^2 having an area equal to a to its right, that is,

$$P(\chi^2 > \chi_a^2) = a$$

Example 14.2
Use Table 3 to find the following critical values of χ^2:

	a	d.f.	χ_a^2
a.	.05	2	_____
b.	.01	20	_____
c.	.025	15	_____
d.	.005	24	_____

To find the critical value of χ^2 used for testing, the degrees of freedom must be known. In the particular situation for which we are using Pearson's statistic, these degrees of freedom are calculated as $(r - 1)(c - 1)$ where r is the number of rows in the contingency table and c is the number of columns.

Example 14.3
The contingency table presented in example 14.1 is shown again. Each cell contains the observed number of offenders (O) together with an estimate of the expected cell frequency, E (in parentheses).

A: completed 6th grade or less
B: completed 7th, 8th or 9th grade
C: completed 10th, 11th, or 12th grade
D: education beyond 12th grade

Margin answers:

5

5
small

large
rejected
large

nonsymmetric
0

5.99147
37.5662
27.4884
45.5585

Number of Arrests	Educational Achievement				Total
	A	B	C	D	
1	55 (45.39)	40 (43.03)	43 (43.03)	30 (36.55)	168
2	15 (21.61)	25 (20.49)	18 (20.49)	22 (17.40)	80
3 or more	7 (10.00)	8 (9.48)	12 (9.48)	10 (8.05)	37
Total	77	73	73	62	285

Before we are able to calculate the observed value of X^2, it is necessary to obtain the expected cell counts. They cannot be obtained exactly, but an *estimate* of the expected cell count for a given cell is calculated as

$$\hat{E} = \text{estimated expected cell count}$$

$$= \frac{(\text{row total})(\text{column total})}{n}$$

For this data, the estimated expected cell counts are calculated as follows:

Category	Estimated Expected Cell Counts
1, A	$\dfrac{168(77)}{285} = 45.39$
1, B	$\dfrac{168(\underline{\quad\quad})}{285} = \underline{\quad\quad}$
3 or more, C	$\dfrac{37(73)}{285} = 9.48$
3 or more, D	$\dfrac{(\underline{\quad\quad})}{285} = \underline{\quad\quad}$

73; 43.03

37; 62; 8.05

Other values for $\hat{E}$ are calculated in a similar manner. Pearson's statistic can now be calculated as

$$X^2 = \Sigma \frac{(O - E)^2}{E} \approx \Sigma \frac{(O - \hat{E})^2}{\hat{E}}$$

$$= \frac{(55 - 45.39)^2}{45.39} + \frac{(40 - 43.03)^2}{43.03} + \ldots + \frac{(12 - 9.48)^2}{9.48} + \frac{(10 - 8.05)^2}{8.05}$$

$$= 10.23$$

The number of degrees of freedom associated with X^2 are

$$(r - 1)(c - 1) = (\underline{\hspace{1cm}})(\underline{\hspace{1cm}}) = \underline{\hspace{1cm}}$$

2; 3; 6

The rejection region, with $\alpha = .05$, is found in Table 3 indexing d.f. = \underline{\hspace{1cm}} and a = \underline{\hspace{1cm}}. We will reject H_0 if $X^2 \geqslant$ \underline{\hspace{1cm}}. Since the observed value is $X^2 = 10.23$, we (do, do not) reject H_0. The data (do, do not) present sufficient evidence to indicate that educational achievement and the number of arrests are dependent.

6

.05; 12.5916

do not; do not

Example 14.4
A sociologist wishes to test the hypothesis that the number of children in a family is independent of the family income. A random sample of 385 families resulted in the following contingency table:

Number of Children	Income Brackets (in thousands of dollars)				Total
	0-$6	$6-12	$12-18	Above $18	
0	10 (14.26)	9 (15.05)	18 (16.48)	24 (15.21)	61
1	8 (17.77)	12 (18.75)	25 (20.53)	31 (18.95)	76
2	14 (21.74)	28 (22.95)	23 (25.12)	28 (23.19)	93
3	26 (17.77)	24 (18.75)	20 (20.53)	6 (18.95)	76
4 or more	32 (18.47)	22 (19.49)	18 (21.34)	7 (19.70)	79
Total	90	95	104	96	385

If the number in parentheses is the estimated expected cell number, do these data present sufficient evidence at the $\alpha = .01$ level to indicate an independence of family size and family income?

Solution
The estimated cell counts have been found by using

$$\hat{E} = \frac{(\text{row total})(\text{column total})}{n}$$

12

and are given in the parentheses within each cell. The degrees of freedom are $(r-1)(c-1) = $ _____ .

1. H_0: the two classifications are independent.
2. H_a: the classifications are not independent.
3. Test statistic:

$$X^2 = \Sigma \frac{(O - \hat{E})^2}{\hat{E}}$$

4. Rejection region: With 12 degrees of freedom, we will reject H_0 if

26.2170

$$X^2 > \chi^2_{.01} = \underline{\hspace{2cm}}$$

Calculate X^2:

$$X^2 = \frac{(10 - 14.26)^2}{14.26} + \frac{(9 - 15.05)^2}{15.05} + \ldots + \frac{(18 - 21.34)^2}{21.34}$$

$$+ \frac{(7 - 19.70)^2}{19.70}$$

$$= 63.4783$$

Reject
are not

5. Decision: (Reject, Do not reject) H_0. Therefore, we can conclude that family size and family income (are, are not) independent classifications.

Example 14.5
Fifty 5th grade students from each of four city schools were given a standardized 5th grade reading test. After grading, each student was rated as satisfactory or not satisfactory in reading ability, with the following results:

	School			
	1	*2*	*3*	*4*
Not satisfactory	7	10	13	6

Is there sufficient evidence to indicate that the percentage of 5th grade students with an unsatisfactory reading ability varies from school to school?

Solution
The preceding table displays only half the pertinent information. Extend the table to include the satisfactory category, allowing space to write in the expected cell frequencies.

	School				
	1	2	3	4	Total
Satisfactory	7 (9)	10 (_____)	13 (_____)	6 (_____)	36
Not satisfactory	43 (_____)	40 (41)	37 (_____)	44 (_____)	164
Total	50	50	50	50	200

9; 9; 9

41; 41; 41

By fixing the column total at 50, we have made certain that each school will be equally represented in our random sampling.

Proceeding with the required test we have the following:

H_0: classifications are independent
H_a: classifications are dependent

Test statistic: $X^2 = \Sigma \dfrac{(O - \hat{E})^2}{\hat{E}}$

Rejection region: For $(2 - 1)(4 - 1) =$ _____ degrees of freedom, we will reject H_0 if $X^2 > \chi^2_{.05} =$ _____.

To calculate the value of the test statistic, we must first find the estimated expected cell counts.

3

7.81473

$\hat{E}$(satisfactory) = (36)(50)/200 = _____
$\hat{E}$(not satisfactory) = (164)(50)/200 = _____

9

41

Then

$$X^2 = \frac{(7-9)^2}{9} + \frac{(10-9)^2}{9} + \frac{(\underline{\quad})^2}{9} + \frac{(6-9)^2}{9}$$

13 – 9

$$+ \frac{(43-41)^2}{41} + \frac{(40-41)^2}{41} + \frac{(\underline{\quad})^2}{41} + \frac{(44-41)^2}{41}$$

37 – 41

$$= \frac{\overline{\quad\quad}}{9} + \frac{\overline{\quad\quad}}{41} = 3.3333 + .7317 = \underline{\quad}$$

30; 30; 4.065

Decision: Since $X^2 = 4.0650 < \chi^2_{.05} = 7.8147$, we (can, <u>cannot</u>) reject the hypothesis that reading ability for 5th graders as measured by this test does not vary from school to school.

cannot

The use of Pearson's statistic to analyze a two-way contingency table is only one of its many uses. Since the beginning student is most likely to run across this type of application, we have presented it in this chapter. The student who is interested in other types of application is referred to the references at the end of chapter 14 in the text.

Self-Correcting Exercises 14A

1. On the basis of the following data, is there a significant relationship between levels of income and political party affiliation at the $\alpha = .05$ level of significance?

Party Affiliation	Income		
	Low	Average	High
Republican	33	85	27
Democrat	19	71	56
Other	22	25	13

2. Three hundred people were interviewed to determine their opinions regarding a uniform driving code for all states.

Sex	Opinion	
	For	Against
Male	114	60
Female	87	39

Is there sufficient evidence to indicate that the opinion expressed is dependent on the sex of the person interviewed?

EXERCISES

1. A serum thought to be effective in preventing colds was administered to 500 individuals. Their records for 1 year were compared to those of 500 untreated individuals, with the following results:

	No Colds	One Cold	More than One Cold
Treated	252	146	102
Untreated	224	136	140

Test the hypothesis that the two classifications are independent, at the $\alpha = .05$ level of significance.

2. A manufacturer wished to know whether the number of defectives produced varied for four different production lines. A random sample of 100 items was selected from each line and the number of defectives recorded:

	Production line			
	1	*2*	*3*	*4*
Defectives	8	12	7	9

Do these data produce sufficient evidence to indicate that the percentage of defectives varies from line to line?

3. In a random sample of 50 male and 50 female undergraduates, each member was asked if he or she was for, against, or indifferent to the practice of having unannounced in-class quizzes. Do the following data indicate that attitude toward this practice is dependent on the sex of the student interviewed?

	Male	*Female*
For	20	10
Against	15	30
Indifferent	15	10

4. A survey of voter sentiment was conducted in four midcity political wards to compare the fraction of voters favoring a "city manager" form of government. Random samples of 200 voters were polled in each of the four wards, with results as follows:

	Ward			
	1	*2*	*3*	*4*
Favor	75	63	69	58
Against	125	137	131	142

Can you conclude that the fractions favoring the city manager form of government differ in the four wards?

5. A personnel manager of a large company investigating employee satisfaction with assigned jobs collected the following data for 200 employees in each of four job categories:

	Categories				
Satisfaction	*I*	*II*	*III*	*IV*	*Total*
High	40	60	52	48	200
Medium	103	87	82	88	360
Low	57	53	66	64	240
Total	200	200	200	200	

Do these data indicate that the satisfaction scores are dependent on the job categories? (Use $\alpha = .05$.)

6. To determine whether dependency in only children (singletons) is related to the mother's age at time of birth, a survey was conducted on 160 kindergarten children from a large city. On the basis of a test, the children were classified as low, average, or high dependency. The results are shown below.

	Dependency Classification		
Mother's Age	Low	Average	High
Under 25	7	26	8
25–32	10	30	9
33–40	12	10	18
Over 40	4	9	17

Do the data indicate that the mother's age and dependency are related? (Test at $\alpha = .10$.)

Chapter   15

NONPARAMETRIC STATISTICS

15.1 Introduction

In earlier chapters we tested various hypotheses concerning populations in terms of their parameters. These tests represent a group of tests that are called _____ tests, since they specifically involve parameters such as means, variances, or proportions. To apply the techniques of chapters 6, 7, and 8, large number of observations were required to assure the approximate _____ of the statistics employed in testing. In chapters 9, 10, 12, and 13, it was assumed that the sampled populations had _____ distributions. Further, if two or more population means were studied in the same experiment, it was necessary to assume that these populations had a common _____. In this chapter we will be concerned with hypotheses that do not involve population parameters directly but deal rather with the form of the distribution. The hypothesis that two distributions are identical versus the hypothesis that one distribution has typically larger values than the other are nonparametric statements of H_0 and H_a.

   Nonparametric tests are appropriate in many situations where one or more of the following conditions exist:

1. Nonparametric methods can be used when the form of the distribution is unknown, so that descriptive parameters may be of little use.
2. Nonparametric techniques are particularly appropriate if the measurement scale is that of rank ordering. This type of data, known as _____ data is very common in the behavioral sciences.
3. If a response can be measured on a continuous scale, a nonparametric method may nevertheless be desirable because of its relative simplicity when compared to its parametric analogue.
4. Most parametric tests require that the sampled population satisfy certain as-

parametric

normality

normal

variance

ordinal

sumptions. When an experimenter cannot reasonably expect that these assumptions are met, a nonparametric test would be a valid alternative. Nonparametric tests can be applied in many situations when parametric tests are inappropriate. Moreover, they are computationally simple to apply. However, since assumptions required for the use of nonparametric tests are less specific than those required for parametric tests, we might expect a nonparametric test to be (more, less) efficient than a corresponding parametric test when all the conditions required for the use of the parametric test are met.

less

In this chapter we will present several nonparametric tests to be used in the comparison of two populations, in the case of paired observations (see section 11.2) and in the situation where two independent random samples have been taken. The final section will deal with a nonparametric measure of association equivalent to the coefficient of correlation, $\hat{\rho}$, presented in chapter 10.

15.2 The Sign Test for Comparing Two Populations

signs

The sign test is based on the _____ of the observed differences. Thus in a paired-difference experiment, we may observe in each pair only whether the first element is larger (or smaller) than the second. If the first element is larger (smaller), we assign a plus (minus) sign to the difference. We will define the test statistic y to be the number of _____ signs observed.

plus

It is worth emphasizing that the sign test *does not* require a numerical measure of a response but merely a statement of which of two responses within a matched pair is larger. Thus the sign test is a convenient and even necessary tool in many psychological investigations. If within a given pair it is impossible to tell which response is larger (a tie occurs), the pair is omitted. Thus if 20 differences are analyzed and 2 of them are impossible to classify as plus or minus, we will base our inference on _____ (give number) differences.

18

Let p denote the probability that a difference selected at random from the population of differences would be given a plus sign. If the two population distributions are identical, the probability of a plus sign for a given pair would equal _____. Then the null hypothesis, "the two populations are identical," could be stated in the form $H_0 : p = \frac{1}{2}$.

½

Recall that in section 7.3 of the text, we presented a large sample test of the null hypothesis $H_0 : p = p_0$, using as a test statistic

$$z = \frac{\hat{p} - p_0}{\sqrt{\dfrac{p_0 q_0}{n}}}$$

where $\hat{p} = y/n$. This test was valid as long as np and nq were greater than 10. However, this normal approximation to binomial probabilities is reasonably accurate when $p = \frac{1}{2}$ even when n is as small as _____. If H_0 is true and $p = \frac{1}{2}$, the test statistic given above can be rewritten as

10

$$z = \frac{\hat{p} - \frac{1}{2}}{\sqrt{\frac{(\frac{1}{2})(\frac{1}{2})}{n}}} = \frac{\frac{y}{n} - .5}{\sqrt{\frac{.25}{n}}}$$

$$= \frac{y - .5n}{\sqrt{.25n}}$$

If the alternative hypothesis is $H_a: p > \frac{1}{2}$, then large (positive, negative) values | positive
of z would be placed in the rejection region. If the alternative hypothesis is $H_a:$
$p < \frac{1}{2}$, then large (positive, negative) values of y would be used in the rejection | negative
region. With $H_a: p \neq \frac{1}{2}$, the rejection region would include both _____ | positive
and _____ values of z. | negative

Example 15.1

Thirty matched pairs of schizophrenic patients were used in an experiment to
determine the effect of a certain drug on sociability. In 18 of these pairs, the patient receiving the drug was judged to be more sociable, while in 5 pairs it was
not possible to detect a difference in sociability. Test to determine whether or
not this drug tends to increase sociability.

Solution

Let p denote the probability that, in a matched pair selected at random, the patient receiving the drug will be more sociable. Further, let y denote the number
of pairs in which the drugged patient is more sociable.
1. The null hypothesis that the two populations are identical is stated as $H_0: p$
    = _____. The alternative hypothesis that the drugged patients will be | ½
    more sociable can be written as $H_a:$ _____. | $p > \frac{1}{2}$
2. The test statistic is

$$z = \frac{y - .5n}{\sqrt{.25n}}$$

    where y is the number of responses in which the drugged patient was more so-
    ciable out of the $n = $ _____ pairs in which a difference was detected. | 25
    For this example, $y = $ _____. | 18
3. Using large (positive, negative) values of z as a rejection region with $\alpha = .05$, | positive
    we will reject H_0 if $z > $ _____. This will be taken as the rejection | 1.645
    region.
4. The observed value of the test statistic is

$$z = \frac{y - .5n}{\sqrt{.25n}} = \frac{\underline{\qquad} - .5(\underline{\qquad})}{\sqrt{.25(\underline{\qquad})}}$$

| 18; 25

| 25

6.25

$$= \frac{18 - 12.5}{\sqrt{\rule{2cm}{0pt}}}$$

2.5; 2.2

$$= \frac{5.5}{\rule{2cm}{0pt}} = \rule{2cm}{0pt}$$

is; reject

5. Since $z = 2.2$ (is, is not) in the rejection region, we (reject, do not reject) H_0 and conclude that the drug tends to increase sociability among schizophrenics.

Example 15.2
The productivity of 35 students was observed and measured both before and after the installation of new lighting in their classroom. The productivity of 21 of the 35 students was observed to have improved while the productivity of the others appeared to show no perceptible gain as a result of the new lighting. It is necessary to determine whether or not the new lighting was effective in increasing student productivity.

Solution
Let p denote the probability that one of the 35 students selected at random exhibits increased productivity after the installation of new lighting. This constitutes a paired-difference test where the productivity measures are paired on the students. Such pairing tends to block out student variations.

$= \frac{1}{2}$
$> \frac{1}{2}$

1. The null hypothesis is $H_0: p$ _____.
2. The appropriate one-sided alternative hypothesis is $H_a: p$ _____.
3. If y denotes the number of students who show improved productivity after the installation of the new lighting, then the test statistic can be taken to be

$$z = \frac{y - .5n}{\sqrt{.25n}}$$

17.5

35

$$= \frac{y - \rule{1.5cm}{0pt}}{\sqrt{.25\,(\rule{1.5cm}{0pt})}}$$

1.645

4. Reject H_0 at the $\alpha = .05$ level of significance if the calculated value of z is greater than $z_{.05}$ = _____.
5. Since $y = 21$,

1.18

$$z = \frac{21 - 17.5}{\sqrt{8.75}} = \rule{2cm}{0pt}$$

would not; has not

Hence we (would, would not) reject H_0; the new lighting (has, has not) improved student productivity.
Notice that the sign test is a comparatively simple test. It requires only one

piece of information from the sample, namely, the number of pairs for which the observation from sample 1 exceeds that from sample 2. It makes no assumptions about the nature of the distribution of measurements, nor does it require that the measurements be numerically valued. However, in gaining this simplicity, we have lost information concerning the magnitude of the differences between samples 1 and 2. Having done so, it will be more difficult for us to detect a difference (when it exists) in two populations using the sign test rather than other tests. If the difference *can* be detected using the sign test, we have found a quick and simple answer to our question.

Self-Correcting Exercises 15A

1. An experiment was designed to compare the durabilities of two highway paints, paint *A* and paint *B,* under actual highway conditions. An *A* strip and a *B* strip were painted across a highway at each of 30 locations. At the end of the test period, the experimenter observed the following results: At 8 locations paint *A* showed the least wear; at 17 locations paint *B* showed the least wear; and at the other 5 locations the paint samples showed the same amount of wear. Can we conclude that paint *B* is more durable? (Use $\alpha = .05$.)

2. Rootstock of varieties *A* and *B* was tested for resistance to nematode intrusion. An *A* and a *B* were planted side by side in each of 12 widely separated locations. At the conclusion of the experiment, all roots were brought into the laboratory for a nematode count. The results are recorded in the following table.

						Location						
	1	2	3	4	5	6	7	8	9	10	11	12
Variety *A*	463	268	871	730	474	432	538	305	173	592	529	321
Variety *B*	277	130	522	610	482	340	319	266	205	540	462	342

Can it be said that varieties *A* and *B* differ in their resistance to nematode intrusion? (Use a two-tailed sign test, with $\alpha = .01$.)

3. An experimenter housed experimental animals two per cage. His experiment required that he randomly choose one of the animals in each cage as a control. His chance device was to reach into the cage and select, as the animal to be treated, the one he was able to catch most easily. In questioning his "random selection," a fellow experimenter weighed each of the animals selected, as well as their cage mates, and found that 12 of the 15 animals selected were the larger or heavier of the pair. Is this sufficient evidence to indicate that the investigator's selection was in fact nonrandom?

15.3 Wilcoxon's Signed-Rank Test

In section 15.2 we discussed one nonparametric test which could be used for a paired-difference experiment. The _____ test requires only the direction of the difference within each matched pair, and therefore (does, does not) require that the measurements be numerically valued. A more efficient test is available if the experimenter has a paired-difference experiment in which the measurement scale is at least _____ (rank ordering). He can test the hypothesis that the two underlying distributions are identical versus the alternative that they are not identical by using Wilcoxon's signed-rank test.

sign
does not

ordinal

In order to calculate the test statistic required for this test, the following procedure is used. Let y_1 denote an observation from sample 1 and let y_2 denote the observation from sample 2 corresponding to the same pair. For each pair, the difference $d = y_1 - y_2$ is calculated. These differences are now ranked from smallest to largest according to their _____ values (ignoring the sign of the difference).

absolute

1. A zero difference is treated as it was in the sign test; the pair is omitted from consideration.
2. Tied differences are assigned a rank equal to the average of the ranks they _would_ have received had they not been tied.

We now define

$$T_+ = \text{sum of the ranks of the positive differences}$$
$$T_- = \text{sum of the ranks of the negative differences}$$

smaller

The test statistic for the Wilcoxon signed-rank test is T, the (smaller, larger) of T_+ and T_-.

If H_0 is true and the two underlying distributions are identical, then there should be as many positive as negative differences. Moreover, the high and low ranks, corresponding to the largest and smallest differences, should be evenly divided between T_+ and T_-. Hence, T_+ and T_- should be approximately the same in value. If either T_+ or T_- is unusually small, the validity of the null hypothesis would be in doubt.

Critical values of T necessary for rejection of the null hypothesis in favor of the two-tailed alternative hypothesis are given in Table 8 of the Appendix in your text, for $n = 5$ to $n = 50$ pairs and various values of α, using the column marked "two-sided." "One-sided" alternative hypotheses can be tested using values of α in the column marked "one-sided" to determine the appropriate rejection region.

Example 15.3
Twelve matched pairs of brain-damaged children were formed for an experiment to determine which of two forms of physical therapy is the more effective. One child was chosen at random from each pair and treated over a period of several months using therapy A, while the other child was treated during this

period using therapy *B*. There was judged to be no difference within two of the matched pairs at the end of the treatment period. The results are summarized in the following table:

Pair	Difference Favorable to Treatment	Rank for the Absolute Value of the Difference
1	A	9
2	A	5
3	B	1.5
4	A	4
5	A	1.5
6	*	*
7	A	7
8	A	8
9	*	*
10	A	10
11	A	6
12	A	3

*zero difference

For a two-sided test with $\alpha = .05$, we should reject H_0, "treatments equally effective," when $T \leqslant$ _____ . The sample value of T is _____ . Hence we _____ H_0. There (is, is not) a difference in the two forms of physical therapy.

8; 1.5

reject; is

Example 15.4

A drug was developed for reducing the cholesterol level in heart patients. The cholesterol levels before and after drug treatment were obtained for a random sample of 25 heart patients, with the following results:

Patient	Cholesterol Level Before	After	Patient	Cholesterol Level Before	After
1	257	243	13	364	343
2	222	217	14	210	217
3	177	174	15	263	243
4	258	260	16	214	198
5	294	295	17	392	388
6	244	236	18	370	357
7	390	383	19	310	299
8	247	233	20	255	258
9	409	410	21	281	276
10	214	216	22	294	295
11	217	210	23	257	227
12	340	335	24	227	231
			25	385	374

It is necessary to determine whether or not this drug has an effect on the cholesterol level of heart patients.

Solution

Differences, Before – After, arranged in order of their absolute values are shown below together with the corresponding ranks. Fill in the missing ranks.

Difference	Rank	Difference	Rank
–1	2	7	14
–1	2	–7	14
–1	2	7	14
–2	4.5	8	16
–2	4.5	11	
3	6.5	11	
–3	6.5	13	19
–4	8.5	14	
4	8.5	14	
5	11	16	
5	11	20	23
5	11	21	24
		30	25

17.5
17.5

20.5
20.5
22

Suppose that the alternative hypothesis of interest to the experimenter is the statement "the drug has the effect of reducing cholesterol levels in heart patients." If H_a is true, we would expect to observe many large positive differences and only a few small negative differences. We would expect to observe a small value for T_-. Consulting Table 8 for $n = 25$, $\alpha = .05$ and a "one-sided" test, H_0 will be rejected if $T \leqslant$ _____. For this example, $T_- =$ _____ and $T_+ =$ _____. Hence the test statistic, $T =$ _____ falls in the rejection region. We reject H_0 in favor of the alternative hypothesis that the drug has the effect of reducing cholesterol levels in heart patients.

101; 44
281; 44

It is interesting to see what conclusion is obtained by using the sign test. Recall that y is equal to the number of positive differences and that the test statistic

$$z = \frac{y - .5n}{\sqrt{.25n}}$$

standard normal

> 1.645; 1.8

has approximately the _____ _____ distribution when n is greater than ten and $H_0: p = 1/2$ is true. With $\alpha = .05$, the rejection region for z is z _____. But $y = 17$, so that $z =$ _____. Thus we obtain the same conclusion as before, though the sample value of the test statistic does not penetrate as deeply into the rejection region as when the Wilcoxon test was used. Since the Wilcoxon test makes fuller use of the information available in the experiment, we say that the Wilcoxon test is more _____ than the sign test.

efficient

Self-Correcting Exercises 15B

1. The sign test is not as efficient as the Wilcoxon signed-rank test for data of the type presented in exercise 2, Self-Correcting Exercises 15A. Analyze the

data of exercise 2, Self-Correcting Exercises 15A by using the two-tailed Wilcoxon signed-rank test with $\alpha = .02$. Can it be said that varieties A and B differ in their resistance to nematode intrusion?

2. The sign test is sometimes used as a "quick and easy" substitute for more powerful tests that require lengthy computations. The following differences were obtained in a paired-difference experiment: $-.93, .95, .52, -.26, -.75,$ $.25, 1.08, 1.47, .60, 1.20, -.65, -.15, 2.50, 1.22, .80, 1.27, 1.46, 3.05,$ $-.43, 1.82, -.56, 1.08, -.16, 2.64$. Use the sign test with $\alpha = .05$ to test for a difference in the two populations.

3. Refer to exercise 2. Use the large-sample Wilcoxon test with $\alpha = .05$ to test for the difference in the two populations. Compare (in efficiency and in computational requirements) the sign test and the Wilcoxon test as substitute tests in a paired-difference experiment.

15.4 Wilcoxon's Rank-Sum Test

If an experimenter has two independent (not related) random samples in which the measurement scale is at least rank ordering, he can test the hypothesis that the two underlying distributions are identical versus the alternative that they are not identical by using Wilcoxon's rank-sum test.

If two independent random samples are drawn from the same population (this is the case if H_0 is true), then we really have one large sample of size $n = n_1 + n_2$. If all measurements were ranked from small (1) to large (n), and each observation from sample 1 replaced with an A while each observation from sample 2 was replaced with a B, we would expect to find the A's and B's randomly mixed in the ranking positions. If H_0 is false and the second sample comes from a population whose values tend to be larger than the first population, the B's would tend to occupy the _____ ranks. However, if the second sample comes from a population whose values tend to be smaller than the first, then the B's would appear in the _____ rank positions.

higher

lower

A statistic that reflects the positions of the n_1 and n_2 sample values in the total ranking is the sum of the ranks occupied by the first sample or the sum of the ranks occupied by the second sample. For the sake of consistency, we will define the test statistic as T, the sum of the ranks occupied by the first sample.

Example 15.5

Suppose that we have two samples each of size 5 with the following values:

Sample A: 19, 20, 16, 12, 23
Sample B: 17, 21, 22, 25, 18

1. Ranking all $n = 10$ observations, we have

	A	A	B	B	A	A	B	B	A	B
	12	16	17	18	19	20	21	22	23	25
Rank	1	2	3	4	5	6	7	8	9	10

2. The sum of the ranks for sample A is

$$T = 1 + 2 + 5 + 6 + 9 = 23$$

When n_1 and n_2 are large ($n_1 \geqslant 10$ and $n_2 \geqslant 10$), the test statistic T has an approximately normal distribution with

$$\mu_T = \frac{n_1(n_1 + n_2 + 1)}{2}$$

$$\sigma_T^2 = \frac{n_1 n_2 (n_1 + n_2 + 1)}{12}$$

and the quantity

$$z = \frac{T - \mu_T}{\sigma_T}$$

has approximately the standard normal distribution. Rejection regions for one- or two-tailed alternatives and various values of α are based on the standard normal distribution.

Example 15.6
A manufacturer uses a large amount of a certain chemical. Since there are just two suppliers of this chemical, the manufacturer wishes to test whether the percentage of contaminants is the same for the two sources against the alternative that there is a difference in the percentage of contaminants for the two suppliers. Data from independent random samples are given below:

Supplier	Contaminant Percentages				
A	.86	.69	.72	.65	1.13
	.65	1.18	.45	1.41	.50
	1.04	.41			
B	.55	.40	.22	.58	.16
	.07	.09	.16	.26	.36
	.20	.15			

Solution

1. We combine the obtained contaminant percentages in a single ordered arrangement and identify each percentage by letter. Ties are handled as in the case of the Wilcoxon signed-rank test.

Percentage	.07	.09	.15	.16	.16	.20	.22	.26
Rank	1	2	3	4.5	4.5	6	7	8
Supplier	B	B	B	B	B	B	B	B
Percentage	.36	.40	.41	.45	.50	.55	.58	.65
Rank	9	10	11	12	13	14	15	16.5
Supplier	B	B	A	A	A	B	B	A
Percentage	.65	.69	.72	.86	1.04	1.13	1.18	1.41
Rank	16.5	18	19	20	21	22	23	24
Supplier	A	A	A	A	A	A	A	A

2. Since the sample sizes of $n_1 = 12$ and $n_2 = 12$ are large, we can use the normal approximation to the distribution of T. The manufacturer, in asking whether there is a difference between the two suppliers, has specified a _____ tailed test. Therefore, we would reject H_0 if T were either too large or too small.

    two-

3. Calculate

$$T = 11 + 12 + 13 + 16.5 + \ldots + 24 = 216$$

$$\mu_T = \frac{n_1(n_1 + n_2 + 1)}{2}$$

$$= \frac{12(25)}{2} = 150$$

$$\sigma_T^2 = \frac{n_1 n_2(n_1 + n_2 + 1)}{12} = \frac{12(12)(25)}{12} = 300$$

4. The rejection region in terms of $z = (T - \mu_T)/\sigma_T$ would be $|z| > 1.96$ for $\alpha = .05$. The observed value of z is

$$z = \frac{T - \mu_T}{\sigma_T} = \frac{\rule{1cm}{0.4pt} - 150}{\sqrt{\rule{1cm}{0.4pt}}}$$

    216

    300

$$= \frac{\rule{1.5cm}{0.4pt}}{17.32} = \rule{1.5cm}{0.4pt}$$

    66; 3.81

Hence there (is, is not) a significant difference in contaminant percentages for the two suppliers.

    is

Use of the Wilcoxon rank-sum test eliminates the need for the restrictive assumptions of the Student's t test, which requires that the samples be randomly drawn from _____ populations having _____ variances.

normal; equal

Self-Correcting Exercises 15C

1. In a deprivation study to test the strength of two physiological drives, 20 rats who were fed the same diet according to a feeding schedule were randomly divided into two groups of 10 rats. Group I was deprived of water for 18 hours and group II was deprived of food for 18 hours. At the end of this time, each rat was put into a maze having the appropriate reward at the exit, and the time required to run the maze was recorded for each rat. The results follow, with time measured in seconds:

Water	Food
16.8	20.8
22.5	24.7
18.2	19.4
13.1	28.9
20.2	25.3
19.3	20.1
17.5	19.3
16.1	20.3
20.3	28.6
19.6	20.1

Is there a difference in strength of these two drives as measured by the time required to find the incentive reward? (Use the Wilcoxon rank-sum test with $\alpha \approx .05$.)

2. Before filling several new teaching positions at the high school level, the principal of the school formed a review board consisting of five teachers who were asked to interview the 21 applicants and rank them in order of merit. Eleven of the 21 applicants held college degrees but had limited teaching experience. Of the remaining 10 applicants, all had college degrees and substantial experience. The review board's rankings are given below.

Limited Experience	Substantial Experience
14	1
6	2
7	3
9	15
10	8
11	5
12	13
4	21
16	20
18	19
17	

Do these rankings indicate that the review board considers experience a prime factor in the selection of the best candidates?

15.5 Spearman's Rank Correlation Coefficient

The Spearman rank correlation coefficient, $\hat{\rho}_s$, is a numerical measure of the association between two variables. As implied in the name of the test statistic, $\hat{\rho}_s$ makes use of _____ and hence the exact value of numerical measurements on the variables need not be known. Conveniently, $\hat{\rho}_s$ is computed in exactly the same manner as _____ , chapter 10.

ranks

$\hat{\rho}$

To determine whether two variables are related, we select a _____ sample of n experimental units (or items) from the population of interest. Each of the n items is ranked first according to the first variable and then according to the second variable. Thus for each item in the experiment, we obtain two _____ . (Tied ranks are treated as in other parts of this chapter.) Let x and y denote the respective ranks assigned to a particular item. Then, as in chapter 10,

random

ranks

$$\hat{\rho}_s = \frac{S_{xy}}{\sqrt{S_{xx}S_{yy}}}$$

Example 15.7

An investigator wished to determine whether "leadership ability" is related to the amount of a certain hormone present in the blood. Six individuals were selected at random from the membership of the Junior Chamber of Commerce in a large city and ranked on the characteristic leadership ability. A determination of hormone content for each individual was made from blood samples. The leadership ranks and hormone measurements are recorded in the following table. Fill in the missing hormone ranks. Note that no difference in leadership ability could be detected for individuals 2 and 5.

Individual	Leadership Ability Rank (y)	Hormone Content	Hormone Rank (x)	
1	6	131	1	
2	3.5	174	_____	3
3	1	189	_____	5
4	2	200	6	
5	3.5	186	_____	4
6	5	156	_____	2

To calculate $\hat{\rho}_s$ we form an auxiliary table. Fill in the missing quantities.

Individual	y	y^2	x	x^2	xy
1	6	_____	1	1	6
2	3.5	12.25	3	9	_____
3	1	1	5	_____	5
4	2	4	_____	36	12
5	_____	12.25	4	16	14
6	5	25	2	4	_____
Total	_____	90.5	21	91	57.5

36
10.5
25
6
3.5
10
21

Thus

$$S_{xy} = 57.5 - (21)(21)/6$$

–16

$$= \underline{\hspace{2cm}}$$

$$S_{xx} = 91 - (21)^2/6$$

17.5

$$= \underline{\hspace{2cm}}$$

$$S_{yy} = 90.5 - (21)^2/6$$

17

$$= \underline{\hspace{2cm}}$$

Finally,

17

$$\hat{\rho}_s = \frac{-16}{\sqrt{(17.5)\,(\underline{\hspace{1.5cm}})}} = -.93$$

Thus high leadership ability (reflected in a low rank) seems to be associated with higher amounts of hormone.

When there are no ties appearing in the data, an alternative formula is available for calculating $\hat{\rho}_s$. Let d be the difference between the ranks x and y for a particular item. With $d = x - y$, the shortcut formula is

$$\hat{\rho}_s = 1 - \frac{6\Sigma d^2}{n(n^2 - 1)}$$

Example 15.8
Mathematics and art aptitude tests were given to each of eight students. The results are given in the following table.

Student	Math	Art
1	23	53
2	37	63
3	36	42
4	38	49
5	42	51
6	58	65
7	60	71
8	66	74

Calculate the Spearman rank correlation coefficient using two different methods and compare the two results.

Solution

1. Rank the mathematics and art scores to obtain the ranks x and y.

Student	x	y
1	1	4
2	3	5
3	2	1
4	4	2
5	5	3
6	6	6
7	7	7
8	8	8

2. Calculate

$$\Sigma x = 36 \quad \Sigma y = 36 \quad \Sigma xy = 193$$
$$\Sigma x^2 = 204 \quad \Sigma y^2 = 204 \quad n = 8$$

Then

$$S_{xy} = \underline{\hspace{2cm}} - \frac{(36)^2}{8} = \underline{\hspace{2cm}}$$ $193; 31$

$$S_{xx} = 204 - \frac{(36)^2}{8} = \underline{\hspace{2cm}}$$ 42

$$S_{yy} = 204 - \frac{(36)^2}{8} = \underline{\hspace{2cm}}$$ 42

and

$$\hat{\rho}_s = \frac{S_{xy}}{\sqrt{S_{xx}S_{yy}}} = \frac{31}{\underline{\hspace{2cm}}} = \underline{\hspace{2cm}}$$ $42; .738$

3. Using the alternative formula, the differences $d = x - y$ are calculated.

Student	1	2	3	4	5	6	7	8
d	-3	-2	1	2	2	0	0	0

Then

$$\Sigma d^2 = 22$$

22

$$\hat{\rho}_s = 1 - \frac{6\,(\underline{\hspace{2cm}})}{8\,(8^2 - 1)}$$

$$= 1 - \frac{132}{\underline{\hspace{2cm}}}$$

504

.738

$$= 1 - .262 = \underline{\hspace{2cm}}$$

Even if ties do occur, very little error will result using the alternate formula, as long as the number of ties is small relative to the number of data points. The Spearman rank correlation coefficient may be employed as a test statistic to

no association

test an hypothesis of _____ between two characteristics. The test statistic is

$$z = \hat{\rho}_s \sqrt{n - 1}$$

10

which has an approximate standard normal distribution for $n \geqslant$ _____. One- or two-tailed rejection regions can be formed depending upon the question of interest to the experimenter.

Example 15.9

Sixteen experimental animals have been trained to activate a simple mechanism which releases a quantity of food. Each animal was then placed in an individual cage with a mechanism which released an amount of a desirable food each time that the mechanism was activated. An alternative, but less desirable, food was also present in each cage. On the fourth day that the animals were in the individual cages, the number of times the mechanisms were activated was obtained. The results were as given in the following table.

Units of food released	1	1	2	2	3	3	4	4	5	5	6	6	7	7	8	8
Number of activations	5	7	6	9	12	11	16	14	16	17	10	12	7	4	3	5

Does it appear that there is a negative association between the number of activations and the amount of food presented to the animal? (Use $\alpha = .05$.)

Solution

1. Spearman's rank correlation coefficient is calculated after ranking the two variables from 1 to 16.

Animal	x	y		Animal	x	y
1	1.5	3.5		9	9.5	14.5
2	1.5	6.5		10	9.5	16
3	3.5	5		11	11.5	9
4	3.5	8		12	11.5	11.5
5	5.5	11.5		13	13.5	6.5
6	5.5	10		14	13.5	2
7	7.5	14.5		15	15.5	1
8	7.5	13		16	15.5	3.5

Calculate

$\Sigma x = 136$ $\Sigma y = $ _____ $\Sigma xy = $ _____   136; 1095

$\Sigma x^2 = $ _____ $\Sigma y^2 = 1494$ $n = 16$ 1492

$$S_{xy} = \underline{\hspace{2cm}} - \frac{(\underline{\hspace{1.5cm}})}{16} = -61 \qquad\qquad 1095; 136$$

$$S_{xx} = \underline{\hspace{2cm}} - 1156 = 336 \qquad\qquad 1492$$

$$S_{yy} = 1494 - 1156 = \underline{\hspace{2cm}} \qquad\qquad 338$$

Then

$$\hat{\rho}_s = \frac{S_{xy}}{\sqrt{S_{xx}S_{yy}}} = \frac{-61}{\sqrt{336(338)}} = \frac{-61}{336.999} = \underline{\hspace{1.5cm}} \qquad\qquad -.181$$

2. To test the hypothesis

$$H_0: \rho_s = 0$$
$$H_a: \rho_s < 0$$

The test statistic is calculated as

$$z = \hat{\rho}_s \sqrt{n - 1}$$

$$= \underline{\hspace{1.5cm}} \sqrt{15} = \underline{\hspace{1.5cm}} \qquad\qquad -.181; -.70$$

3. The rejection region is in the (upper, lower) tail of the standard normal distribution. For $\alpha = .05$, H_0 is rejected if z _____ .

    lower
    < -1.645

is not
is not

4. Since the observed value of z is not in the rejection region, H_0 (is, is not) rejected. There (is, is not) sufficient evidence to indicate $\rho_s < 0$.

Self-Correcting Exercises 15D

1. An interviewer was asked to rank 12 applicants as to their suitability for a given position. The same 12 applicants took a written examination that was designed to rate an applicant's ability to function in the given position. The interviewer's ranking and the examination score for each applicant are given below.

Applicant	Interview Rank	Examination Score
1	4	49
2	7	42
3	5	58
4	3	50
5	6	33
6	2	65
7	1	67
8	10	46
9	9	52
10	11	61
11	8	64
12	12	43

Calculate the value of Spearman's rank correlation coefficient for these data. Test for a significant negative rank correlation at the $\alpha = .05$ level of significance.

2. A manufacturing plant is considering building a subsidiary plant in another location. Ten plant sites are currently under consideration. After considering land and building costs, zoning regulations, available local work force, and transportation facilities associated with each possible plant site, two corporate executives have independently ranked the 10 possible plant sites as follows:

	Site									
	1	2	3	4	5	6	7	8	9	10
Executive 1	2	7	9	5	3	10	4	8	6	1
Executive 2	1	4	10	6	2	9	7	8	5	3

a. Calculate Spearman's rank correlation coefficient between the two sets of rankings.
b. Is there reason to believe the two executives are in basic agreement regarding their evaluation of the 10 plant sites? (Use $\alpha = .05$.)

EXERCISES

1. For each of the following tests, state whether the test would be used for related samples or for independent samples: sign test, Wilcoxon signed-rank test, Wilcoxon rank-sum test.

2. About 1.2% of our combat forces in a certain area develop combat fatigue. To find identifying characteristics of men who are predisposed to this breakdown, the level of a certain adrenal chemical was measured in samples from two groups: men who had developed battle fatigue and men who had adjusted readily to combat conditions. The following determinations were recorded:

Battle fatigue group	23.35	21.08	22.36	20.24
	21.69	21.54	21.26	20.71
	20.00	23.40	21.43	21.54
	22.21			
Well-adjusted group	21.66	21.85	21.01	20.54
	20.19	19.26	21.16	19.97
	20.40	19.92	20.52	19.78
	21.15			

Use a Wilcoxon rank-sum test with α equal to .05 to test whether the distributions of levels of this chemical are the same in the two groups against the alternative that the mean level is not the same in the two groups.

3. To test the effect of an experimental drug on perception time, 25 subjects were tested by recording the length of time in seconds between the presentation of a light stimulus and the recording of that stimulus by the subject under test. The subject was tested twice, once before and once after ingesting the drug. The results of the experiment follow.

Subject	Before	After	Subject	Before	After
1	8.3	7.8	14	7.6	7.7
2	7.8	9.0	15	9.7	6.1
3	9.8	6.1	16	8.4	9.2
4	6.7	6.9	17	9.6	7.0
5	7.5	6.3	18	11.3	9.3
6	6.1	7.0	19	12.0	9.5
7	9.4	7.2	20	8.5	8.0
8	11.3	9.8	21	7.9	6.2
9	12.1	10.3	22	8.8	9.4
10	9.8	7.2	23	10.3	8.9
11	6.8	7.8	24	11.2	9.1
12	9.2	8.8	25	6.9	8.8
13	10.1	9.2			

Do these data indicate that the drug decreases the perception time? (Use the signed-rank test.)

4. The value of $\hat{\rho}$ (defined in chapter 10) for the following data is .636:

1	2
.05	1.08
.14	1.15
.24	1.27
.30	1.33
.47	1.41
.52	1.46
.57	1.54
.61	2.72
.67	4.01
.72	9.63

Calculate $\hat{\rho}_s$ for these data. What advantage of $\hat{\rho}_s$ was brought out in this example?

5. A ranking of the quarterbacks in the top 10 teams of the National Football League was made by polling a number of professional football coaches and sportswriters. This "true ranking" is shown below together with my ranking.
   a. Calculate $\hat{\rho}_s$.
   b. Do the data provide evidence at the $\alpha = .05$ level of significance to indicate a positive correlation between my ranking and that of the experts?

	Quarterback									
	A	B	C	D	E	F	G	H	I	J
True ranking	10	2	3	4	5	6	7	8	1	9
My ranking	9	1	4	5	2	8	6	7	3	10

6. To investigate a possible age difference in authoritarian views for adolescent males, written tests for assessing authoritarianism were given to 11 males aged 12–14 years and 13 males aged 15–17. Do the following data indicate that males for the age group 15–17 years have stronger authoritarian views than the younger group (i.e., higher scores)? (Use the rank-sum test.)

12–14	15–17
83	48
71	112
32	59
67	94
40	76
52	110
88	85
26	55
97	85
60	93
63	81
	100
	64

7. Eleven recent college graduates have interviewed for positions within the marketing department of a large industrial organization. The organization's vice-president for marketing and the personnel director rated each candidate independently on a 0–10 assumed-interval scale. Their ratings are shown below. Use a two-tailed sign test to determine if the vice-president and the personnel manager differ in their evaluations of the 11 candidates. (Use $\alpha = .05$.)

	Candidate										
	1	*2*	*3*	*4*	*5*	*6*	*7*	*8*	*9*	*10*	*11*
Vice-president	4	7	8	9	7	4	3	8	6	6	7
Personnel manager	2	4	5	5	8	1	5	6	7	3	8

8. Refer to exercise 7 and analyze the data using the two-tailed Wilcoxon signed-rank test with $\alpha = .05$. Explain any differences in conclusions arrived at using the Wilcoxon versus the sign test. Which conclusion should we believe?

9. It is of interest to determine whether the efficiency of a certain machine operator is superior to the efficiency of another. To examine this question, the percentages of defective items produced daily by machine operators A and B are recorded over a period of time. More recorded data are available from operator A due to a recent illness experienced by operator B. The data are shown below.

	Percentage of Output Defective										
Operator *A*	3	2	7	6	5	5	3	7	4	6	8	9
Operator *B*	6	5	8	4	8	7	9	10	9	9		

The plant analyst realizes that distributions of percentages do not follow a normal distribution and is hesitant to use a t test in the analysis. Use the most powerful nonparametric test at your disposal to determine whether operator A produces a lower percentage defective than operator B. (Use $\alpha = .05$.)

SOLUTIONS TO
SELF-CORRECTING EXERCISES

Set 2A

1. a. The height of each bar represents the total civilian labor force for the year of interest and the shaded area represents the proportion employed.

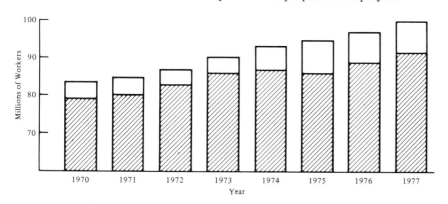

b. In order to make the drop in employment in 1975 look large, the vertical scale must be stretched and perhaps should begin at the point "70 million workers."

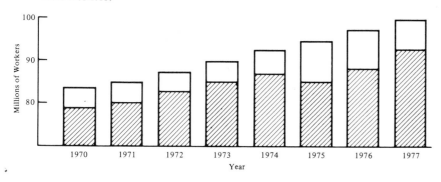

2. For each subdivision, the number of degrees in the central angle of its sector is given below.

Group	Degrees
White collar	(43.7) (360)/87.5 = 180
Blue collar	(29.0) (360)/87.5 = 119
Service worker	(12.0) (360)/87.5 = 49
Farm worker	(2.8) (360)/87.5 = 12

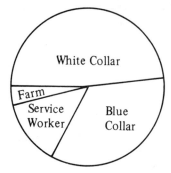

3. a. For each of the three years, a separate circle chart is constructed. Sector angles for the five subdivisions are given in the table below.

	Sector Angles		
	1977	1978	1979
	y(360)	y(360)	y(360)
	50.7	52.5	54.5
United States	130	130	130
West Europe	102	97	95
Japan	38	40	41
Canada	15	15	15
Other	75	77	79

The three circle charts are shown below. Notice that the relative amounts demanded remain almost identical, while the actual amounts demanded increase over the three years.

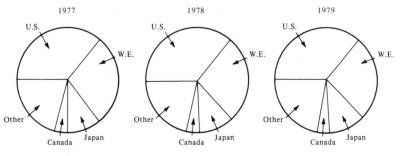

b. Using a bar chart, countries are represented on the horizontal axis with each bar subdivided to show demands for 1977 (shaded) and 1979.

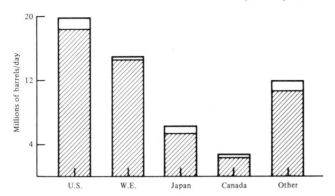

c. Bar charts are more effective, since they do show the slight projected increase in demand while the circle charts do not.

Set 2B

1. a. range = 59 – 18 = 41.
   b.–c. Each student will obtain slightly different results. Dividing the range by 10 produces intervals of length slightly more than 4. A more convenient choice is to use 11 intervals of length 4, beginning at 17.5.

Class	Class Boundaries	Tally	f_i
1	17.5–21.5	||||	4
2	21.5–25.5	||||	4
3	25.5–29.5	卌 |	6
4	29.5–33.5	卌 ||	7
5	33.5–37.5	卌 |	6
6	37.5–41.5	||||	4
7	41.5–45.5	||||	4
8	45.5–49.5	||	2
9	49.5–53.5	|||	3
10	53.5–57.5	|	1
11	57.5–61.5	|	1

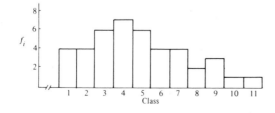

d. Dividing the range by 6, each interval must be of length 7.

Class	Class Boundaries	Tally	f_i
1	17.5–24.5	Ⅲ II	7
2	24.5–31.5	Ⅲ Ⅲ	10
3	31.5–38.5	Ⅲ Ⅲ I	11
4	38.5–45.5	Ⅲ II	7
5	45.5–52.5	IIII	5
6	52.5–59.5	II	2

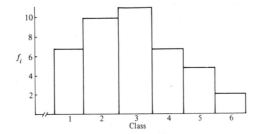

e. The second histogram is more informative, since it exhibits the "piling up" of the data in the middle classes. Using too many classes tends to "flatten out" the histogram, producing nearly equal frequencies in each class.

2. a. An extra column in the tabulation is used to calculate relative frequency.

Class	Class Boundaries	Tally	f_i	f_i/n
1	5.55–7.55	Ⅲ	5	5/32
2	7.55–9.55	Ⅲ	5	5/32
3	9.55–11.55	Ⅲ Ⅲ II	12	12/32
4	11.55–13.55	Ⅲ	5	5/32
5	13.55–15.55	III	3	3/32
6	15.55–17.55	I	1	1/32
7	17.55–19.55	I	1	1/32

b. Refer to part a, and connect the midpoints of the classes at the proper height to form the relative frequency polygon.

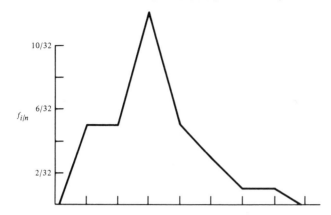

c. $(1/32) + (1/32) = 2/32.$
d. $(5/32) + (5/32) = 10/32.$
e. $(12/32) + (5/32) + (3/32) = 20/32.$

Set 3A

1. Arrange the set of data in order of ascending magnitude:

6	9	11	13	16
8	10	12	13	17
9	10	12	15	19

median $= 12; \bar{y} = \Sigma y/n = 180/15 = 12.$

2. Arrange the data in order of ascending magnitude.

y	$(y - \bar{y})$	$(y - \bar{y})^2$
0	-3	9
1	-2	4
2	-1	1
2	-1	1
2	-1	1
3	0	0
3	0	0
4	1	1
4	1	1
5	2	4
7	4	16
33	0	38

a. median = 3, $\bar{y} = 33/11 = 3$.

b. range = $7 - 0 = 7$.

c. $s^2 = \Sigma(y-\bar{y})^2/(n-1) = 38/10 = 3.8$; $s = \sqrt{3.8} = 1.95$.

Set 3B

1. Display the data in a table as follows:

y	y^2
0	0
1	1
2	4
2	4
2	4
3	9
3	9
4	16
4	16
5	25
7	49
33	137

$$s^2 = \frac{\Sigma y^2 - (\Sigma y)^2/n}{n-1}$$

$$= \frac{137 - (33)^2/11}{10}$$

$$= \frac{137 - 99}{10} = \frac{38}{10} = 3.8.$$

2. If $\bar{y}$ has been rounded off, then rounding error occurs each time $\bar{y}$ is subtracted from y in formula a. Hence there are n possible rounding errors. If formula b is used, only one rounding error occurs when $(\Sigma y)^2$ is divided by n. Hence formula b is less subject to rounding errors and results in a more accurate computation.

3. $\Sigma y = 29.7$, $\Sigma y^2 = 129.19$,

$$s^2 = \frac{\Sigma y^2 - (\Sigma y)^2/n}{n-1} = \frac{129.19 - (29.7)^2/7}{6} = \frac{129.19 - 126.0129}{6}$$

$$= \frac{3.1771}{6} = .5295,$$

$$s = \sqrt{.5295} = .73.$$

4. $\Sigma y = 356$, $\Sigma y^2 = 25{,}362$,

$$s^2 = \frac{25{,}362 - (356)^2/5}{4} = \frac{25{,}362 - 25{,}347.2}{4} = \frac{14.8}{4} = 3.7,$$

$$\bar{y} = \frac{356}{5} = 71.2.$$

5. a. The interval of interest is $\mu \pm 2\sigma = 26 \pm 2(1)$ or 24 to 28. According to the Empirical Rule, approximately 95% of all subjects should identify this number correctly.

  b. The percentage of interest is the percentage lying to the left of the point $\mu - \sigma$. Since approximately 68% of the measurements lie within the interval $\mu \pm \sigma$, 32% should fall outside of this interval. Then, because of the symmetry of a mound-shaped distribution, $^{32}/_2 = 16\%$ of the measurements lie to the left of $\mu - \sigma = 25$. Hence, the probability that a subject picked at random will identify 25 or fewer colors is .16.

Set 4A

1. Let y be the number of apartment dwellers who move within a year. Then $p = P$ (move within a year) $= .2$ and $n = 7$.

  a. $P(y = 2) = \dfrac{7!}{2!5!}(.2)^2 (.8)^5 = .27525$.

  b. $P(y \leqslant 1) = \dfrac{7!}{0!7!}(.2)^0 (.8)^7 + \dfrac{7!}{1!6!}(.2)^1 (.8)^6 = .209715 + .367002 = .57617$.

2. Let y be the number of subjects reverting to the first method learned. Then $p = P$ (revert to first method) $= .8$ and $n = 6$.

  $$P(y \geqslant 5) = P(5) + P(6)$$

  $$= \frac{6!}{5!1!}(.8)^5 (.2)^1 + \frac{6!}{6!0!}(.8)^6 (.2)^0$$

  $$= .393216 + .262144$$

  $$= .65536$$

3. Let y be the number of accepted applicants taking a place in the freshman class, so that $p = .9$ and $n = 1{,}360$; $\mu = np = 1{,}360(.9) = 1{,}224$; $\sigma = \sqrt{npq} = \sqrt{122.4} = 11.06$. The freshman class limits are $\mu \pm 2\sigma = 1{,}224 \pm 22.12$, or $1{,}201.88$ to $1{,}246.12$. Choosing the largest interval with integer endpoints within these limits, the class will be between $1{,}202$ and $1{,}246$ in size.

4. Let y be the number of minority members on a list of 80, so that $p = .20$ and $n = 80$. Then $\mu = 80(.2) = 16$ and $\sigma = \sqrt{npq} = \sqrt{12.8} = 3.58$. The limits are $\mu \pm 2\sigma = 16 \pm 7.16$, or 8.84 to 23.16. We expect to see between 9 and 23 minority group members on the jury lists.

5. y = number watching the TV program; $p = .4$; $n = 400$; $\mu = 400(.4) = 160$;

$\sigma^2 = 400(.4)(.6) = 96$; $\sigma = \sqrt{96} = 9.80$. Calculate $\mu \pm 2\sigma = 160 \pm 2(9.8)$ $= 160 \pm 19.6$, or 140.4 to 179.6. Since we would expect the number watching the show to be between 141 and 179 with probability .95, it is highly unlikely that only 96 people would have watched the show *if* the 40% claim is correct. It is more likely that the percentage of viewers for this particular show is less than 40%.

6. Let y be the number of fines given a student in 6 days, so that $p = P(\text{fine}) = .10$.

a. $P(y = 0) = \dfrac{6!}{0!6!}(.10)^0 (.9)^6 = .531441.$

b. P (fines less than or equal to $3.00) = P(y \leqslant 2)$

$= P(0) + P(1) + P(2)$

$= .531441 + \dfrac{6!}{1!5!}(.1)^1 (.9)^5 + \dfrac{6!}{2!4!}(.1)^2 (.9)^4$

$= .531441 + .354294 + .098415$

$= .98415.$

Set 4B

Note: The student should illustrate each problem with a diagram and list all pertinent information before attempting the solution. Diagrams are omitted here in order to conserve space.

1. a. $P(z > 2.1) = .5000 - A(2.1) = .5000 - .4821 = .0179.$

b. $P(z < -1.2) = .5000 - A(1.2) = .5000 - .3849 = .1151.$

c. $P(.5 < z < 1.5) = P(0 < z < 1.5) - P(0 < z < .5) = A(1.5) - A(.5)$
$= .4332 - .1915 = .2417.$

d. $P(-2.75 < z < -1.70) = A(2.75) - A(1.7) = .4970 - .4554 = .0416.$

e. $P(-1.96 < z < 1.96) = A(1.96) + A(1.96) = 2(.4750) = .95.$

f. $P(z > 1.645) = .5000 - A(1.645) = .5000 - .4500 = .05.$

Linear interpolation was used in part f. That is, since the value $z = 1.645$

is halfway between two table values, $z = 1.64$ and $z = 1.65$, the appropriate area is taken to be halfway between the two table areas, $A(1.64) = .4495$ and $A(1.65) = .4505$. As a general rule, values of z will be rounded to two decimal places, except for this particular example, which will occur frequently in our calculations.

2. a. We know that $P(z > z_0) = .10$, or $.5000 - A(z_0) = .10$, which implies that $A(z_0) = .4000$. The value of z_0 that satisfies this equation is $z_0 = 1.28$, so that $P(z > 1.28) = .10$.

   b. $P(z < z_0) = .01$ so that $.5000 - A(z_0) = .01$ and $A(z_0) = .4900$. The value of z_0 that satisfies this equation is $z_0 = -2.33$, so that $P(z < -2.33) = .01$. The student who draws a diagram will see that z_0 must be negative, since it must be in the left-hand portion of the curve.

   c. $P(-z_0 < z < z_0) = A(z_0) + A(z_0) = .95$ so that $A(z_0) = .4750$. The necessary value of z_0 is $z_0 = 1.96$ and $P(-1.96 < z < 1.96) = .95$.

   d. $P(-z_0 < z < z_0) = 2A(z_0) = .99$ so that $A(z_0) = .4950$. The necessary value of z_0 is $z_0 = 2.58$ and $P(-2.58 < z < 2.58) = .99$.

3. The random variable of interest has a standard normal distribution and hence may be denoted as z.

   a. $P(z > 1) = .5000 - A(1) = .5000 - .3413 = .1587$.

   b. $P(z > 1.5) = .5000 - A(1.5) = .5000 - .4332 = .0668$.

   c. $P(-1 < z < -.5) = A(1) - A(.5) = .3413 - .1915 = .1498$.

   d. The problem is to find a value of z, say z_0, such that $P(-z_0 < z < z_0) = .95$. This was done in 2c and $z_0 = 1.96$. Hence 95% of the billing errors will be between \$-1.96 and \$1.96.

   e. Undercharges imply negative errors. Hence the problem is to find z_0 such that $P(z < z_0) = .05$. That is, $.5000 - A(z_0) = .05$, or $A(z_0) = .4500$. The value of z_0 is $z_0 = -1.645$ (see 1f) and hence 5% of the undercharges will be at least \$1.65.

4. We have $\mu = 10$, $\sigma = \sqrt{2.25} = 1.5$.

   a. $P(y > 8.5) = P\left(\dfrac{y - \mu}{\sigma} > \dfrac{8.5 - 10}{1.5}\right)$

   $= P(z > -1)$

   $= .5000 + A(1) = .5000 + .3413$

   $= .8413$.

b. $P(y < 12) = P\left(z < \dfrac{12 - 10}{1.5}\right)$

$\qquad = P(z < 1.33) = .5000 + A(1.33)$

$\qquad = .5000 + .4082 = .9082.$

c. $P(9.25 < y < 11.25)$

$\qquad = P\left(\dfrac{9.25 - 10}{1.5} < z < \dfrac{11.25 - 10}{1.5}\right)$

$\qquad = P(-.5 < z < .83) = .1915 + .2967 = .4882.$

d. $P(7.5 < y < 9.2) = P(-1.67 < z < -.53)$

$\qquad\qquad\qquad\qquad = .4525 - .2019 = .2506.$

e. $P(12.25 < y < 13.25)$

$\qquad = P(1.5 < z < 2.17)$

$\qquad = .4850 - .4332 = .0518.$

5. The random variable of interest is y, the length of life for a standard household light bulb. It is normally distributed with $\mu = 250$ and $\sigma = \sqrt{2{,}500} = 50$.

a. $P(y > 300) = P\left(z > \dfrac{300 - 250}{50}\right) = P(z > 1)$

$\qquad\qquad\qquad = .5000 - .3413 = .1587.$

b. $P(190 < y < 270) = P(-1.2 < z < .4)$

$\qquad\qquad\qquad\qquad = .3849 + .1554 = .5403.$

c. $P(y < 260) = P(z < .2) = .5000 + .0793$

$\qquad\qquad\qquad\qquad = .5793$

d. It is necessary to find a value of y, say y_0, such that $P(y > y_0) = .90$. Now

$P(y > y_0) = P\left(\dfrac{y - \mu}{\sigma} > \dfrac{y_0 - 250}{50}\right) = .90$, so that

$P\left(z > \dfrac{y_0 - 250}{50}\right) = .5 + A\left(\dfrac{y_0 - 250}{50}\right)$

$\qquad\qquad\qquad = .90,$ or

$A\left(\dfrac{y_0 - 250}{50}\right) = .40.$

By looking at a diagram, the student will notice that the value satisfying this equation must be negative. From Table 3, this value, $(y_0 - 250)/50$, is $(y_0 - 250)/50 = -1.28$, or $y_0 = -1.28(50) + 250 = 186$. Ninety percent of the bulbs have a useful life in excess of 186 hours.

e. Similar to d. It is necessary to find y_0 such that $P(y < y_0) = .95$. Now

$$P(y < y_0) = P\left(z < \frac{y_0 - 250}{50}\right) = .95,$$

$$.5000 + A\left(\frac{y_0 - 250}{50}\right) = .95, \text{ and}$$

$$A\left(\frac{y_0 - 250}{50}\right) = .45.$$

Hence $(y_0 - 250)/50 = 1.645$, or $y_0 = 332.25$. That is, 95% of all bulbs will burn out before 332.25 hours.

6. The random variable is y, scores on a trade school entrance examination, and has a normal distribution with $\mu = 50$ and $\sigma = 5$.

a. $P(y > 60) = P\left(z > \dfrac{60 - 50}{5}\right)$

$\quad = P(z > 2) = .5000 - .4772$

$\quad = .0228.$

b. $P(y < 45) = P(z < -1) = .5000 - .3413$

$\quad = .1587.$

c. $P(35 < y < 65) = P(-3 < z < 3)$

$\quad = .4987 + .4987 = .9974.$

d. It is necessary to find y_0 such that $P(y < y_0) = .95$. As in 2e, $A(y_0 - 50/5) = .45.\ (y_0 - 50)/5 = 1.645$, or $y_0 = 58.225.$

Set 5A

1. Assign random numbers 01 through 99 to accounts no. 1 through no. 99 and assign random number 00 to account no. 100. Randomly select 20 random numbers and sample the associated accounts.

2. a. Using three digit numbers 001 through 250 to identify the $N = 250$ workers, we could use the random digits 001 through 250 to identify the workers to be included in the sample, and for any three digit random number in the range 251 through 999 use its remainder upon division by

250. For example, worker number 200 would be associated with the random numbers 200, 450, 700 and 950. Worker number 250 would be associated with the random digits 250, 500, 750 and 000.

b. Suppose a random starting point was determined as line 11, column 5 of the random number table in your text. The first three digits of lines 11–16 in columns 5–10 are

196	780	916	469	575	222
228	626	703	585	178	801
176	636	233	670	923	504
473	001	745	462	066	237
273	696	717	035	756	215

The remainders after division by 250 are

196	030	166	219	075	222
228	126	203	085	178	101
176	136	233	170	173	004
223	001	245	212	066	237
023	196	017	035	006	215

Therefore, the 30 workers associated with the above numbers are to be included in the sample.

Set 5B

1. a. According to the Central Limit Theorem, $\bar{y}$ is approximately normally distributed with $\mu_{\bar{y}} = \mu = 6$ and variance $\sigma_{\bar{y}}^2 = \sigma^2/n = 36/40 = .9$.
   b. Standardizing $\bar{y}$ using $z = (\bar{y} - \mu_{\bar{y}})/\sigma_{\bar{y}}$, we obtain

$$P(\bar{y} > 7.5) = P\left(z > \frac{7.5 - 6}{\sqrt{.9}}\right)$$

$$= P(z > 1.58) = .5 - .4429 = .0571.$$

   c. According to the Empirical Rule, 95% of all the measurements lie within two standard deviations of the mean. Since a standard deviation is $\sigma_{\bar{y}} = \sqrt{0.9} = .95$, we would expect most values of $\bar{y}$ to lie in the interval $\mu_{\bar{y}} \pm 2\sigma_{\bar{y}} = 6 \pm 2(.95)$ or 4.1 to 7.9.

2. a. Similar to exercise 1c. Calculate $\sigma_{\bar{y}} = \sigma/\sqrt{n} = 1/6 = .1667$. Most values of $\bar{y}$ should lie in the interval $\mu_{\bar{y}} \pm 2\sigma_{\bar{y}} = 5.7 \pm 2(.1667) = 5.7 \pm .33$ or 5.37 to 6.03.
   b. The z value corresponding to $\bar{y} = 6.1$ is $z = (\bar{y} - \mu)/(\sigma/\sqrt{n}) = (6.1 - 5.7)/.1667 = 2.40$ and $P(\bar{y} > 6.1) = P(z > 2.40) = .5 - .4918 = .0082$. This is

a highly unlikely event if in fact $\mu = 5.7$. Perhaps the mean is greater than 5.7.

Set 5C

1. a. $P(8) = \dfrac{10!}{8!2!} (.7)^8 (.3)^2 = .2335.$

   $P(9) = \dfrac{10!}{9!1!} (.7)^9 (.3)^1 = .1211.$

   $P(10) = \dfrac{10}{10!0!} (.7)^{10} (.3)^0 = .0282.$

   Then $P(8 \leqslant y \leqslant 10) = .2335 + .1211 + .0282 = .3828.$

   b. The probabilities associated with the values $y = 8, 9$, and 10 are needed; hence the area of interest is the area to the right of 7.5 and to the left of 10.5. Further, $\mu = np = 7, \sigma^2 = npq = 2.1$.

   $P(8 \leqslant y \leqslant 10) \approx P(7.5 < y < 10.5)$

   $$= P\left(\frac{7.5 - 7}{\sqrt{2.1}} < z < \frac{10.5 - 7}{\sqrt{2.1}} \right)$$

   $$= P(.35 < z < 2.42)$$

   $$= .4922 - .1368 = .3554.$$

2. Let $p = P$ (income is less than 12,000) $= \frac{1}{2}$, since 12,000 is the median income. Also, $n = 100, \mu = np = 50, \sigma^2 = npq = 25.$

   $P(y \leqslant 37) \approx P(y < 37.5)$

   $$= P[z < (37.5 - 50)/5]$$

   $$= P(z < -2.5) = .5000 - .4938 = .0062.$$

   The observed event is highly unlikely under the assumption that \$12,000 is the median income. The \$12,000 figure does not seem reasonable.

3. y = number of white seeds, $p_2 = P$ (white seed) $= .4, n = 100; \mu = np = 40,$ $\sigma^2 = npq = 24, \sigma = 4.90.$

   a. $P(y \leqslant 50) \approx P(y < 50.5)$

   $$= P[z < (50.5 - 40)/4.9]$$

$$= P(z < 2.14)$$

$$= .5 + .4848 = .9838.$$

b. $P(y \leqslant 35) \approx P(y < 35.5) = P(z < -.92)$

$$\doteq .5 - .3212 = .1788.$$

c. $P(25 \leqslant y \leqslant 45) \approx P(24.5 < y < 45.5)$

$$= P(-3.16 < z < 1.12)$$

$$= .5 + .3686 = .8686.$$

4. According to the Central Limit Theorem, $\hat{p}$ is approximately normal with mean $p = .10$ and variance $pq/n = [.1(.9)]/100 = .0009$. Then 95% of all values of $\hat{p}$ should lie in the interval $\mu_{\hat{p}} \pm 2\sigma_{\hat{p}} = .10 \pm 2\sqrt{.0009} = .10 \pm .06$ or .04 to 0.16. The value $\hat{p} = .18$ is an unlikely value, assuming that $p = .10$. Perhaps the percentage of birth defects is greater than 10%.

Set 6A

1. $\bar{y} = 67.5$ with approximate bound on error $2s/\sqrt{n} = 2(8.2)/\sqrt{93} = 1.70$.

2. $\hat{p} = y/n = 31/204 = .15$ with approximate bound on error $2\sqrt{\hat{p}\hat{q}/n} = 2\sqrt{.15(.85)/204} = 2\sqrt{.000625} = .05$.

3. $\hat{p} = y/n = 8/50 = .16$ with approximate bound on error $2\sqrt{\hat{p}\hat{q}/n} = 2\sqrt{.16(.84)/50} = 2(.0518) = .1036$.

4. $\bar{y} = 19.3$ with approximate bound on error $2(s/\sqrt{n}) = 2(5.2/\sqrt{30}) = 1.90$.

Set 6B

1. $\bar{y} \pm z(s/\sqrt{n})$; $89.50 \pm 1.96(25.10/\sqrt{50})$; 89.50 ± 6.96 or 82.54 to 96.46.

2. $\bar{y} \pm z(s/\sqrt{n})$; $8750 \pm 1.96(3050/\sqrt{50})$; 8750 ± 845.42 or 7904.58 to 9595.42.

3. $\hat{p} \pm z\sqrt{\hat{p}\hat{q}/n}$ where $\hat{p} = 30/65 = .46$; $.46 \pm 2.58\sqrt{.46(.54)/65}$; $.46 \pm .16$ or .30 to .62.

4. $\bar{y} \pm zs/\sqrt{n}$; $22 \pm 1.645(4)/\sqrt{39}$; $22 \pm (6.58/6.245)$; 22 ± 1.05, or 20.95 to 23.05.

5. $\hat{p} \pm z\sqrt{\hat{p}\hat{q}/n}$ where $\hat{p} = 25/100 = .25$; $.25 \pm 2.58\sqrt{.25(.75)/100}$; $.25 \pm .11$ or .14 to .36.

Set 7A

1. $H_0: \mu = 3.35; H_a: \mu \neq 3.35$; test statistic:

$z = (\bar{y} - \mu_0)/(s/\sqrt{n})$. With $\alpha = .05$,

reject H_0 if $|z| > 1.96$. Calculate

$\bar{y} = 1,264.40/400 = 3.161$;

$s^2 = (4,970.3282 - 3,996.7684)/399 = 2.4400$;

$s = \sqrt{2.44} = 1.56$;

$z = (\bar{y} - \mu_0)/(s/\sqrt{n}) = \dfrac{3.161 - 3.35}{1.56/20} = -2.42.$

Reject H_0. Mean revenue is different from \$3.35.

2. $H_0: p = \frac{1}{2}; H_a: p \neq 1/2$; test statistic:

$z = (\hat{p} - p_0)/\sqrt{p_0 q_0/n}$.

With $\alpha = .01$, reject H_0 if $|z| > 2.58$. Since $\hat{p} = 480/900 = .533$,

$z = (.533 - .5)/\sqrt{.5(.5)/900} = .033/(.5/30) = 1.98.$

Do not reject H_0. The result is not inconsistent with the null hypothesis.

3. $H_0: p = .5; H_a: p > .5$; test statistic:

$z = (\hat{p} - p_0)/\sqrt{p_0 q_0/n}.$

With $\alpha = .05$, reject H_0 if $z > 1.645$. Since $\hat{p} = 34/65 = .52$,

$z = (.52 - .50)/\sqrt{.5(.5)/65} = .02/.062 = .32.$

H_0 is not rejected. There is insufficient evidence to conclude that the proportion favoring the merger is greater than .5.

4. $H_0: \mu = 25; H_a: \mu > 25$; test statistic:

$z = (\bar{y} - \mu_0)/(\sigma/\sqrt{n})$

With $\alpha = .01$, reject H_0 if $z > 2.33$. It is given that $\sigma = 3$ for the normal inspection procedure. Hence,

$z = (29 - 25)/(3/\sqrt{30}) = 4/.548 = 7.30.$

H_0 is rejected. The first inspector is not working up to company standards.

Set 7B

1. p value $= 2P(\bar{y} < 3.161) = 2P(z < -2.42) = 2(.5 - .4922) = 2(.0078) = .0156$.

   Any researcher specifying an α value greater than or equal to .0156 would reject the null hypothesis.

2. p value $= P(\hat{p} > .52) = P(z > .32) = .5 - .1255 = .3745$.

   Any researcher specifying an α level greater than or equal to .3745 would reject the null hypothesis. Since this value would not generally be acceptable, we would not reject H_0.

3. $H_0: p = .1; H_a: p < .1$; test statistic:

   $$z = (\hat{p} - p_0)/\sqrt{p_0 q_0/n}$$

   where $\hat{p} = y/n = 8/100 = .08$;

   p value $= P(\hat{p} < .08) = P(z < (.08 - .10)/\sqrt{(.1)(.9)/100}) = P(z < -0.67)$
   $= .5 - .2486 = .2514$.

   Since this value is fairly large, the observed result is not unlikely assuming H_0 is true. H_0 is not rejected.

Set 8A

1. $\bar{y}_1 - \bar{y}_2 = 150.5 - 160.2 = -9.7$ with approximate bound on error

   $$2\sqrt{s_1^2/n_1 + s_2^2/n_2} = 2\sqrt{23.72/35 + 36.37/35} = 2\sqrt{1.7169} = 2.62.$$

2. $\hat{p}_1 - \hat{p}_2 = \dfrac{y_1}{n_1} - \dfrac{y_2}{n_2} = \dfrac{31}{204} - \dfrac{41}{191} = .15 - .21 = -.06$.

   Approximate bound on error:

   $$2\sqrt{\frac{\hat{p}_1 \hat{q}_1}{n_1} + \frac{\hat{p}_2 \hat{q}_2}{n_2}} = 2\sqrt{.000625 + .000869} = 2(.039) = .078.$$

3. $\hat{p}_1 = 50/100 = .50; \hat{p}_2 = 60/200 = .30$.

   $$(\hat{p}_1 - \hat{p}_2) \pm 1.96 \sqrt{\frac{\hat{p}_1 \hat{q}_1}{n_1} + \frac{\hat{p}_2 \hat{q}_2}{n_2}}$$

   $$(.50 - .30) \pm 1.96 \sqrt{\frac{.5(.5)}{100} + \frac{.3(.7)}{200}}$$

   $.2 \pm 1.96 (.0596), .2 \pm .12$, or .08 to .32.

4. a. $(\bar{y}_1 - \bar{y}_2) \pm z\sqrt{s_1^2/n_1 + s_2^2/n_2}$,

   $(12,520 - 11,210) \pm 2.58\sqrt{(1,510)^2/90 + (950)^2/60}$,

   $1,310 \pm 2.58 (200.938)$,

   $1,310 \pm 518.42$ or 791.58 to $1,828.42$.

   b. If the two schools belonged to populations having the same mean annual income, then $\mu_1 = \mu_2$, or $\mu_1 - \mu_2 = 0$. This value of $(\mu_1 - \mu_2)$ does not fall in the confidence interval obtained above. Hence it is unlikely that the two schools belong to populations having the same mean annual income.

Set 8B

1. $H_0: \mu_1 - \mu_2 = 0; H_a: \mu_1 - \mu_2 > 0$; test statistic:

   $z = [(\bar{y}_1 - \bar{y}_2) - 0]/\sqrt{s_1^2/n_1 + s_2^2/n_2}$

   With $\alpha = .05$, reject H_0 if $z > 1.645$. Calculate

   $$z = \frac{720 - 693}{\sqrt{104/50 + 85/50}} = 27/1.94 = 13.92.$$

   Reject H_0. There is a significant difference in the mean scores. Men score higher on the average than women.

2. p value $= P(z > 13.92) \approx 0$. Hence, it is almost certain that $\mu_1 > \mu_2$. Reject H_0.

3. $H_0: p_1 - p_2 = 0; H_a: p_1 - p_2 \neq 0$; test statistic:

   $$z = \frac{(\hat{p}_1 - \hat{p}_2) - 0}{\sqrt{\hat{p}\hat{q}(1/n_1 + 1/n_2)}}$$

   Note that if $p_1 = p_2$ as proposed under H_0, the best estimate of this common value of p is

   $\hat{p} = (y_1 + y_2)/(n_1 + n_2) = (16 + 6)/(100 + 50) = .15$.

   With $\alpha = .05$, reject H_0 if $|z| > 1.96$. Calculate

   $$z = \frac{(16/100) - (6/50)}{\sqrt{.15(.85)(1/100 + 1/50)}} = \frac{.04}{.0618} = .65.$$

   Do not reject H_0. There is insufficient evidence to detect a difference in the performances of the machines.

Set 9A

1. $H_0: \mu = 10; H_a: \mu < 10$; test statistic:

   $t = (\bar{y} - \mu)/(s/\sqrt{n})$.

   With $\alpha = .01$ and $n - 1 = 9$ degrees of freedom, reject H_0 if $t < -t_{.01}$ $= -2.821$. Calculate

   $t = (9.4 - 10)/(1.8/\sqrt{10}) = -.6/.57 = -1.05$.

   Do not reject H_0. There is insufficient evidence to claim that the mean weight is less than 10 ounces.

   $\bar{y} \pm t_{.005} \, s/\sqrt{n}, 9.4 \pm 3.25(1.8/\sqrt{10})$,
   9.4 ± 1.85, or 7.55 to 11.25.

2. $H_0: \mu = 35; H_a: \mu > 35$; test statistic:

   $t = (\bar{y} - \mu)/(s/\sqrt{n})$.

   With $\alpha = .05$, and $n - 1 = 19$ degrees of freedom, reject H_0 if $t > t_{.05} = 1.729$. Calculate

   $t = (42 - 35)/(6.2/\sqrt{20}) = 7/1.386 = 5.05$.

   Reject H_0. The mean riding time is greater than 35 minutes.

3. $\bar{y} \pm t_{.025} \, s/\sqrt{n}, 42 \pm 2.093 \, (1.386)$,
   42 ± 2.90, or 39.1 to 44.9.

Set 9B

1. See section 9.4, paragraph 1.

2. $H_0: \mu_1 - \mu_2 = 0$; $H_a: \mu_1 - \mu_2 \neq 0$; test statistic:

   $t = [(\bar{y}_1 - \bar{y}_2) - D_0]/s\sqrt{1/n_1 + 1/n_2}$

   With $\alpha = .05$ and $n_1 + n_2 - 2 = 16 + 9 - 2 = 23$ degrees of freedom, reject H_0 if $|t| > t_{.025} = 2.069$. Calculate

   $$s^2 = \frac{(n_1 - 1) s_1^2 + (n_2 - 1) s_2^2}{n_1 + n_2 - 2}$$

   $$= \frac{15 \, (2.8)^2 + 8 \, (5.3)^2}{23} = \frac{117.6 + 224.72}{23}$$

   $= 14.8835$ and $s = 3.86$.

$$t = \frac{5.2 - 8.7}{3.86\sqrt{\frac{1}{16} + \frac{1}{9}}} = \frac{-3.5}{3.86\,(.42)} = -2.16.$$

Reject H_0. The mean distance to the health center differs for the two groups.

3. $(\bar{y}_1 - \bar{y}_2) \pm t_{.025}s\sqrt{1/n_1 + 1/n_2}$.

   $-3.5 \pm 2.069\,(1.62),\ -3.5 \pm 3.35,\ $ or

   -6.85 to -0.15 miles.

4. $H_0: \mu_1 - \mu_2 = 0; H_a: \mu_1 - \mu_2 \neq 0$; test statistic;

   $t = [(\bar{y}_1 - \bar{y}_2) - D_0]/s\sqrt{1/n_1 + 1/n_2}$.

   With $\alpha = .05$ and $n_1 + n_2 - 2 = 34$ degrees of freedom, reject H_0 if $|t| > t_{.025}$
   $= 1.96$. Calculate

   $s^2 = [(n_1 - 1)s_1^2 + (n_2 - 1)s_2^2]/(n_1 + n_2 - 2)$

   $\quad = [17\,(23.2) + 17\,(19.8)]/34 = 21.5.$

   $t = (81.7 - 77.2)/\sqrt{21.5(2/18)}$

   $\quad = 4.5/1.5456 = 2.91.$

   Reject H_0. There is a difference in mean scores for the two methods.

Set 10A

1. a.

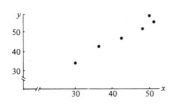

   $\Sigma x = 256 \qquad \Sigma xy = 12,608$
   $\Sigma y = 286 \qquad n = 6$
   $\Sigma x^2 = 11,294 \qquad \Sigma y^2 = 14,096$

   The trend appears to be linear.

   b. $S_{xy} = 12,608 - (256)\,(286)/6 = 405.3333$
   $\quad S_{xx} = 11,294 - (256)^2/6 = 371.3333$
   $\quad \hat{\beta}_1 = S_{xy}/S_{xx} = 405.3333/371.3333 = 1.09$
   $\quad \hat{\beta}_0 = (286/6) - 1.09\,(256/6)$
   $\quad\quad = 47.6667 - 46.5067 = 1.16$

c. $\hat{y} = 1.16 + 1.09\,(50) = 55.66$, or 5566 students.

2. a. $\Sigma x\ = 31.6 \qquad \Sigma xy = 624.6$
$\Sigma y\ = 135 \qquad n = 7$
$\Sigma x^2 = 149.82 \qquad \Sigma y^2 = 2{,}645$
$S_{xy} = 624.6 - (31.6)\,(135)/7 = 15.1714$
$S_{xx} = 149.82 - (316)^2/7 = 7.1686$
$\hat{\beta}_1\ = S_{xy}/S_{xx} = 15.1714/7.1686 = 2.12$
$\hat{\beta}_0\ = 19.29 - 2.12\,(4.51) = 9.73$

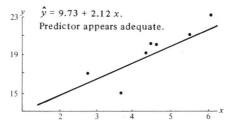

$\hat{y} = 9.73 + 2.12\,x.$
Predictor appears adequate.

3. a. $\Sigma x\ = 96 \qquad \Sigma xy = 1{,}799$
$\Sigma y\ = 135 \qquad n = 7$
$\Sigma x^2 = 1{,}402 \qquad \Sigma y^2 = 2{,}645$
$S_{xy} = 1{,}799 - (96)\,(135)/7 = -52.4286$
$S_{xx} = 1{,}402 = (96)^2/7 = 85.4286$
$\hat{\beta}_1\ = S_{xy}/S_{xx} = -52.4286/85.4286 = -0.61$
$\hat{\beta}_0\ = 19.29 - (-.61)\,(13.71) = 27.65$
$\hat{y}\ = 27.65 - .61x$

b.

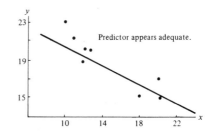

Predictor appears adequate.

Set 10B

1. $s^2 = \dfrac{1}{n-2}(S_{yy} - \hat{\beta}_1 S_{xy}) = \dfrac{1}{n-2}\left[S_{yy} - \dfrac{(S_{xy})^2}{S_{xx}} \right]$

$= \dfrac{1}{4}\left[\left(14{,}096 - \dfrac{(286)^2}{6} \right) - \dfrac{(405.3333)^2}{371.3333} \right]$

$$= \frac{1}{4}(463.33 - 442.45) = \frac{1}{4}(20.88) = 5.22.$$

Note that $\hat{\beta}_1 S_{xy} = (S_{xy})^2/S_{xx}$ has been used for the sake of accuracy.

$s = \sqrt{5.22} = 2.28.$

a. $H_0: \beta_1 = 0; H_a: \beta_1 \neq 0.$
   Reject H_0 if $|t| > t_{.025} = 2.776.$
   Test statistic:

$$t = (\hat{\beta}_1 - \beta_1)/s/\sqrt{S_{xx}} = 1.09/\sqrt{5.22/371.33}$$

$$= \frac{1.09}{.12} = 9.08.$$

   Reject H_0.

b. $\hat{\beta}_1 \pm t_{.025}s/\sqrt{S_{xx}} = 1.09 \pm 2.776\,(.12)$
   $\qquad\qquad\qquad = 1.09 \pm .33, \quad \text{or}$
   $.76 < \beta_1 < 1.42.$

2. $s^2 = \frac{1}{5}[2645 - (1/7)(135)^2 - (15.1714)^2/7.1686]$

   $\quad = \frac{1}{5}(41.43 - 32.11) = \frac{1}{5}(9.32) = 1.86$

   $s = \sqrt{1.86} = 1.36$

   $H_0: \beta_1 = 0; H_a: \beta_1 \neq 0.$

   Rejection region: With 5 degrees of freedom and $\alpha = .05$, reject H_0 if $|t| > t_{.025} = 2.571.$
   Test statistic:

   $t = (\hat{\beta}_1 - 0)/s/\sqrt{S_{xx}} = 2.12/\sqrt{1.86/7.17} = 2.12/.51 = 4.16.$

   Reject H_0.

3. $s^2 = \frac{1}{5}[2645 - (135)^2/7 - (-52.4286)^2/85.4286]$

   $\quad = \frac{1}{5}(41.43 - 32.18) = \frac{1}{5}(9.25) = 1.85$

   $s = \sqrt{1.85} = 1.36$

   $H_0: \beta_1 = 0; H_a: \beta_1 \neq 0.$ Reject H_0 if $|t| > t_{.025} = 2.571.$

   $t = (-.61 - 0)/\sqrt{1.85/85.43} = -.61/.15 = -4.067.$

   Reject H_0.

Set 10C

1. a. $\hat{p} = S_{xy}/\sqrt{S_{xx}S_{yy}}$

    $= 15.1714/\sqrt{(7.1686)\,(41.43)}$

    $= 15.1714/17.2335 = .88.$

   b. $\hat{p}^2 = (.88)^2 = .7744.$ Total variation is reduced by 77.44% by using number of cotton bolls to aid in prediction.

   c. $H_0: \rho = 0; H_a: \rho > 0;$ test statistic:

    $t = \hat{p}\sqrt{(n-2)/(1-\hat{p}^2)} = .88\sqrt{5/[1-(.88)^2]} = 4.16$

    Reject if $t > t_{.05} = 2.015.$ Reject $H_0.$

2. a. $\hat{p} = -52.4286/\sqrt{(85.4286)\,(41.43)}$

    $= -52.4286/59.4921 = -.88.$

    Total variation is reduced by 77.44% by using number of damaging insects to aid in prediction.

   b. The predictors are equally effective.

3.

x_1 (Bolls)	x_2 (Insects)
5.5	11
2.8	20
4.7	13
4.3	12
3.7	18
6.1	10
4.5	12

$\Sigma x_1 = 31.6$

$\Sigma x_1^2 = 149.82$

$n = 7$

$\Sigma x_2 = 96$

$\Sigma x_2^2 = 1,402$

$\Sigma x_1 x_2 = 410.80$

$$\hat{p} = \frac{410.8 - (31.6)\,(96)/7}{\sqrt{(7.1686)\,(85.4286)}} = \frac{-22.5714}{24.7468} = -.91.$$

High correlation explains the fact that either variable is equally effective in predicting cotton yield.

Set 11A

1. $H_0: \mu_d = \mu_P - \mu_H = 0; H_a: \mu_d = \mu_P - \mu_H < 0;$

    test statistic: $t = (\bar{d} - \mu_d)/(s_d/\sqrt{n}).$

    With $\alpha = .05,$ and $n - 1 = 10 - 1 = 9$ degrees of freedom, reject H_0 if $t < -t_{.05} = -1.833.$ The 10 differences and the calculation of the test statistic follow.

d	d^2
-5	25
-2	4
4	16
-3	9
-3	9
1	1
-1	1
0	0
-5	25
1	1
-13	91

$\bar{d} = -13/10 = -1.3,$

$s_d^2 = \dfrac{91 - (-13)^2/10}{9} = \dfrac{74.1}{9} = 8.2333,$

$s_d = \sqrt{8.2333} = 2.869,$

$t = \dfrac{-1.3 - 0}{2.869/\sqrt{10}} = -1.43.$

Do not reject H_0.

2.

d	d^2
4.6	21.16
1.8	3.24
-1.0	1.00
2.2	4.84
1.0	1.00
1.2	1.44
2.6	6.76
2.8	7.84
2.0	4.00
3.0	9.00
20.2	60.28

$\bar{d} = \dfrac{20.2}{10} = 2.02,$

$s_d^2 = \dfrac{60.28 - 40.804}{9} = \dfrac{19.476}{9} = 2.164,$

$s_d = 1.47.$

a. $\bar{d} \pm t_{.025} \dfrac{s_d}{\sqrt{n}}$, $2.02 \pm 2.262 \dfrac{1.47}{\sqrt{10}}$,

2.02 ± 1.05, or $.97 < \mu_d < 3.07$.

b. $H_0: \mu_P - \mu_H = 0; H_a: \mu_P - \mu_H > 0$;

test statistic: $t = (\bar{d} - \mu_d)/(s_d/\sqrt{n})$.

With $\alpha = .05$ and $n - 1 = 9$ degrees of freedom, reject H_0 if $t > 1.833$. Calculate

$t = 2.02/.465 = 4.34$.

Reject H_0. Per-unit scale increases production.

3.

d	d^2
-4	16
-1	1
-10	100
-2	4
-3	9
3	9
-5	25
0	0
-22	164

$\bar{d} = \dfrac{-22}{8} = -2.75$

$s_d^2 = \dfrac{164 - (-22)^2/8}{7}$

$= \dfrac{103.5}{7} = 14.7857$

$s_d = 3.845$

$H_0: \mu_N - \mu_S = 0; H_a: \mu_N - \mu_S < 0$; test statistic:

$t = \dfrac{\bar{d}}{s_d/\sqrt{n}} = \dfrac{-2.75}{3.845/\sqrt{8}} = -2.02.$

With $\alpha = .01$ and $n - 1 = 7$ degrees of freedom, reject H_0 if $t < -2.998$. Do not reject H_0.

Set 11B

1. The estimator of μ is $\bar{y}$, with standard deviation $\sigma/\sqrt{n}$. Hence, solve

$n = 4\sigma^2/B^2 = 4(8^2)/9 = 28.4$.

The experimenter should obtain $n = 29$ measurements.

2. The estimator of p is $\hat{p} = y/n$ with standard deviation $\sqrt{pq/n}$. Since it is given that $0 \leqslant p \leqslant .1$, maximum variation will occur when $p = .1$ and the sample size must be large enough to account for this maximum variation. Hence, solve

$n = 4pq/B^2 = 4(.1)\,(.9)/(.01)^2 = 3600.$

3. With $B = 10$ and $\sigma \approx R/4 = 80/4 = 20$,

$n = 4\sigma^2/B^2 = 4(20^2)/100 = 16.$

4. With $B = .01$ and $p = q \approx 1/2$,

$n = 4pq/B^2 = 4(1/2)(1/2)/(.01)^2 = 10000.$

Set 13A

1. The sample variances are

$s_1^2 = (485 - 462.25)/3 = 7.5833 \qquad s_2^2 = 4.00$

$s_3^2 = 2.9167 \qquad\qquad\qquad s_4^2 = 2.3333$

$s_W^2 = \dfrac{22.75 + 8.00 + 8.75 + 4.6667}{4 + 3 + 4 + 3 - 4}$

$= 44.1667/10 = 4.41667$

$s_B^2 = \dfrac{\Sigma n_i \bar{y}_i^2 - \dfrac{(\Sigma n_i \bar{y}_i)^2}{n}}{k - 1} = \dfrac{4(10.75)^2 + \ldots + 3(5.33)^2 - (105)^2/14}{3}$

$= \dfrac{63.3333}{3} = 21.1111$

$H_0: \mu_1 = \mu_2 = \mu_3 = \mu_4$; test statistic:
$F = s_B^2/s_W^2 = 21.1111/4.4167 = 4.78.$
With $v_1 = 3$ and $v_2 = 10$ reject H_0 if $F > F_{.01} = 6.55$. Do not reject H_0.

2. The numerators of the sample variances are

$(n_1 - 1)s_1^2 = 1.512 \qquad (n_2 - 1)s_2^2 = 4.012 \qquad (n_3 - 1)s_3^2 = 1.252$

$s_W^2 = \dfrac{1.512 + 4.012 + 1.252}{15 - 3} = .5647$

$s_B^2 = 5\left[\dfrac{6.46^2 + 5.64^2 + 6.66^2 - (18.76)^2/3}{2}\right]$

$= (5/2)(.58427) = 1.4607$

$H_0: \mu_1 = \mu_2 = \mu_3$; H_a: at least one of the equalities is incorrect. Test statistic:

$F = s_B^2 / s_W^2$. With $v_1 = 2$ and $v_2 = 12$ degrees of freedom, reject H_0 if $F > F_{.05}$ = 3.89. Since $F = 2.5867$, do not reject H_0. We cannot find a significant difference.

Set 14A

1. H_0: independence of classifications; H_a: classifications are not independent. Expected and observed cell counts are given in the table.

Party Affiliation	Income			
	Low	Average	High	Total
Republican	33 (30.57)	85 (74.77)	27 (39.66)	145
Democrat	19 (30.78)	71 (75.29)	56 (39.93)	146
Other	22 (12.65)	25 (30.94)	13 (16.41)	60
Total	74	181	96	351

With $(r - 1)(c - 1) = 2(2) = 4$ degrees of freedom, reject H_0 if $X^2 > \chi_{.05}^2 = 9.49$. Test statistic:

$$X^2 = \frac{(2.43)^2}{30.57} + \frac{(10.23)^2}{74.77} + \ldots + \frac{(-3.41)^2}{16.41} = 25.61.$$

Reject H_0. There is a significant relationship between income levels and political party affiliation.

2. H_0: opinion independent of sex; H_a: opinion dependent on sex. Expected and observed cell counts are given in the table.

Sex	Opinion		Total
	For	Against	
Male	114 (116.58)	60 (57.42)	174
Female	87 (84.42)	39 (41.58)	126
Total	201	99	300

With $(r - 1)(c - 1) = 1$ degree of freedom and $\alpha = .05$, reject H_0 if $X^2 > \chi_{.05}^2$ = 3.84. The test statistic is

$$X^2 = \frac{(-2.58)^2}{116.58} + \frac{(2.58)^2}{57.42} + \frac{(2.58)^2}{84.42} + \frac{(-2.58)^2}{41.58} = .4119.$$

Do not reject H_0. There is insufficient evidence to show that opinion is dependent on sex.

Set 15A

1. Let $p = P$ (paint A shows less wear) and y = number of locations where paint A shows less wear. Since no numerical measure of a response is given, the sign test is appropriate. $H_0: p = 1/2; H_a: p < 1/2$. Rejection region: With $n = 25, p = 1/2$, reject H_0 if $z < -1.645$ with

$$z = (y - .5n)/\sqrt{.25n} = (8 - 12.5)/2.5 = -1.8.$$

Reject H_0. Paint B is more durable.

2. $H_0: p = 1/2$ where $p = P$ (variety A exceeds variety B). Test statistic:

$$z = (y - .5n)/\sqrt{.25n} = (9 - 6)/\sqrt{3} = 1.73.$$

Rejection region: With $\alpha = .01$, reject H_0 if $|z| > 2.58$. Do not reject H_0.

3. $H_0: p = 1/2; p \neq 1/2$ where $p = P$ (choose heavier animal). Test statistic:

$$z = (y - .5n)/\sqrt{.25n} = (12 - 7.5)/\sqrt{3.75} = 2.32$$

Rejection region: With $\alpha = .05$, reject H_0 if $z > 1.96$. Reject H_0. The selection is not random.

Set 15B

1. H_0: no difference in distribution of number of nematodes for varieties A and $B; H_a$: distribution of number of nematodes differs for varieties A and B. Rank the absolute differences from smallest to largest and calculate T, the smaller of the two (positive and negative) rank sums.

							Location					
	1	2	3	4	5	6	7	8	9	10	11	12
d	186	138	349	120	-8	92	219	39	-32	52	67	-21
Rank $|d|$	10	9	12	8	1	7	11	4	3	5	6	2

Rejection region: With $\alpha = .02$ and a two-sided test, reject H_0 if $T \leqslant 10$. Since $T = 1 + 2 + 3 = 6$, reject H_0. There is a difference between A and B.

2. $H_0: p = 1/2$, where $p = P$ (positive difference) and $n = 24; H_a: p \neq 1/2$. Using $\alpha = .05$ and the normal approximation, H_0 will be rejected if

$|z| > 1.96$ where $z = (y - .5n)/\sqrt{.25n}$ where y = number

of positive differences. Calculate

$$z = (y - 12)/.5\sqrt{24} = (16 - 12)/2.45 = 1.63.$$

Do not reject H_0.

3. The ranks of the absolute differences are given along with their corresponding signs: $-12, 13, 6, -4, -10, 3, 14.5, 20, 8, 16, -9, -1, 22, 17, 11, 18, 19, 24, -5, 21, -7, 14.5, -2, 23$. With $\alpha = .05$ and a two-sided test, reject H_0 if $T \leqslant 81$. Since $T = 50$, reject H_0. Note that the sign test is computationally simple, but the Wilcoxon test is more efficient since it allows us to reject H_0 while the sign test did not.

Set 15C

1. Rank the times from low to high. Note $n_1 = n_2 = 10$.

Water	Food
3	15
16	17
5	8
1	20
12	18
6.5	10.5
4	6.5
2	13.5
13.5	19
9	10.5

Then

$T = 3 + 16 + \ldots + 9 = 72$

$\mu_T = 10(21)/2 = 105$

$\sigma_T^2 = 10^2(21)/12 = 175$

H_0: no difference in the distributions; H_a: the distributions are different. Test statistic:

$z = (T - \mu_T)/\sigma_T = (72 - 105)/\sqrt{175} = -2.49$.

Rejection region: With $\alpha = .05$, reject H_0 if $|z| > 1.96$. Reject H_0. There is a difference between food and water.

2. The data are presented in ranked form, with $T = 124$

$\mu_T = 11(22)/2 = 121$

$\sigma_T^2 = 11(12)(22)/12 = 242$

H_0: no difference in distributions; H_a: ranks for substantial experience are lower than those for limited experience. Test statistic:

$z = (T - \mu_T)/\sigma_T = (124 - 121)/\sqrt{242} = .19$.

Rejection region: With $\alpha = .05$, reject H_0 if $z > 1.645$. Do not reject H_0.

Set 15D

1. Rank the examination scores and note that the interview scores are already in rank order.

Interview Rank (x)	Exam Rank (y)
4	5
7	2
5	8
3	6
6	1
2	11
1	12
10	4
9	7
11	9
8	10
12	3

$\Sigma x = \Sigma y = 78 \qquad \Sigma xy = 450 \qquad \Sigma x^2 = \Sigma y^2 = 650 \qquad n = 12$

$\hat{\rho}_s = (450 - 507)/\sqrt{(650 - 507)^2} = -57/143 = -.399$

$H_0: \rho_s = 0; H_a: \rho_s < 0;$ Test statistic:

$z = \hat{\rho}_s\sqrt{n - 1} = -.399\sqrt{11} = -1.32.$

Reject H_0 if $z < -1.645$ with $\alpha = .05$. Therefore, do not reject H_0.

2. a. $\Sigma x = \Sigma y = 55; \Sigma x^2 = \Sigma y^2 = 385; \Sigma xy = 371.$

$\hat{\rho}_s = (371 - 302.5)/(385 - 302.5) = 68.5/82.5 = .83.$

b. $H_0: \rho_s = 0; H_a: \rho_s > 0;$ Test statistic:

$z = \hat{\rho}_s\sqrt{n - 1} = .83\sqrt{9} = 2.49.$

With $\alpha = .05$, reject H_0 if $z > 1.645$. Therefore, reject H_0. They are in basic agreement.

ANSWERS TO EXERCISES

Chapter 2

1. a. 6.8; c. .80; .55
2. Bar heights for each year represent total sales volume (cash + credit).
3. *Receipts chart:* Individual income taxes—151 degrees; Corporation income taxes—58 degrees; Social insurance receipts—100 degrees; Excise taxes—22 degrees; Borrowing—11 degrees; Other—18 degrees.
   Expenditures chart: Benefit payments—133 degrees; Grants—61 degrees; National defense—105 degrees; Net interest—25 degrees; Other—36 degrees.
4. *1965 chart:* Common stocks—180 degrees; Preferred stocks—36 degrees; Industrial bonds—36 degrees; Government bonds—90 degrees; Mortgages—18 degrees.
   1975 chart: Common stock—118 degrees; Preferred stock—18 degrees; Industrial bonds—54 degrees; Government bonds—118 degrees; Mortgages—72 degrees.
5. Bar height for each year represents total dollar volume (Australia and Great Britain and W. Germany).

Class	Interval	Tally	Frequency	Relative Frequency
1	44.5–53.5	|	1	1/28
2	53.5–62.5	|	1	1/28
3	62.5–71.5	|||||	5	5/28
4	71.5–80.5	|||||	5	5/28
5	80.5–89.5	||||| ||||	9	9/28
6	89.5–98.5	||||| ||	7	7/28
			28	28/28 = 1

Chapter 3

1. a. median = 19.5. b. 10. c. 75 (upper quartile). d. $\bar{y} = 19.03$; $s^2 = 2.7937$; $s = 1.67$. e. Yes, since 70%, 95%, and 100% of the measurements lie in the intervals $\bar{y} \pm ks$, $k = 1, 2, 3$, respectively.
2. a. 16%. b. 81.5%.
3. a. 8. b. 2.45 to 2.95; 5.95 to 6.45.
4. $\mu = 6.6$ ounces.
5. a. $s \approx 16$. b. $\bar{y} = 136.07$; $s^2 = 292.4952$; $s = 17.1$.
6. Answers for this exercise will vary from student to student, but $\bar{y} \approx 1$ and $s \approx .7$. Therefore, the data do not conform to the Empirical Rule.
7. a. s is approximated as 5. b. $\bar{y} = 11.67$; $s^2 = 13.9523$; $s = 3.74$. c. 14/15.
8. a. Approximately 97.4%. b. Approximately 16%.
9. Approximately .025.

Chapter 4

1. a. Approximately 2. b. ¾; ¼.
2. a. .25. b. .383. c. .617. d. .558. e. .692. f. .058. g. .13. h. .80. i. .583.
3. a. $^5/_{32}$. b. $^6/_{32}$.
4. .1493. b. .3828.
5. a. .3277. b. .00672.
6. .0547.
7. a. .9713. b. .1009. c. .7257. d. .9706. e. .8925. f. .5917.
8. a. $z_0 = .70$. b. $z_0 = 2.13$. c. $z_0 = 1.645$. d. $z_0 = 1.55$.
9. a. .8413. b. .8944. c. .9876. d. .0401.
10. 87.48.
11. $\mu = 10.071$.
12. a. .0139. b. .0668. c. .5764. d. .00000269.

Chapter 5

1. No.
2. a. .9838. b. .0000. c. .8686.
3. .3520.
4. a. $110 \pm 2(.99)$ or 108 to 112. b. Approximately 0.
5. a. .1635. b. .0192.
   c. Yes, since $P(y \geqslant 60 \mid p = .2) = .0192$.
6. .0062.

Chapter 6

1. The inference; measure of goodness.
2. Point estimator; interval estimator.
3. 61.23 ± 1.50.
4. $2.705 \pm .012$.
5. $.6 \pm .048$.
6. $\bar{y} = 2.705$; bound $= .009$.
7. $\bar{y} = 21.6$; bound $= .50$.
8. $.2 \pm .0392$.

Chapter 7

2. $z = 2.5$; yes.
3. p value $= .0062$.
4. $z = -5.2$; reject the claim.
5. p value $< .002$.
6. $z = 2.8$; p value $= .0026$; learning is taking place.

Chapter 8

1. The inference; measure of goodness.
2. $.030 \pm .033$.
3. -8 ± 4.49.
4. $z = -4.59$; p value $< .001$; yes.
5. $z = -3.40$; yes.
6. a. $z = 5.8$; yes. b. $3.0 \pm .85$.
7. a. $.56 \pm .05$. b. $-.25 \pm .22$.

Chapter 9

1. According to the Central Limit Theorem, these statistics will be approximately normally distributed for large n.
2. i. The parent population has a normal distribution.
   ii. The sample is a random sample.
3. The number of degrees of freedom associated with a t statistic is the denominator of the estimator of σ^2.
4. Do not reject H_0; $t = -.6$.
5. $2.48 < \mu < 4.92$.
6. Do not reject H_0; $t = 1.16$.
7. $-.76 < \mu_1 - \mu_2 < 3.96$.
8. Do not reject H_0; $t = 1.72$; no.

9. Reject H_0; $t = 3.04$; yes.
10. 40 ± 22.8.
11. Do not reject H_0; $t = 0.13$.

Chapter 10

1.

	y Intercept	Slope
a.	-2	3
b.	0	2
c.	-.5	-1
d.	2.5	-1.5
e.	2	0

2. a. $\hat{y} = 2 - .875x$. c. Reject $H_0: \beta_1 = 0$, since $t = 12.12$. d. $\hat{\rho} = .99$; $\hat{\rho}^2 = .98$. The use of the linear model rather than $\bar{y}$ as a predictor for y reduced the sum of squares for error by 98%.

3. The fitted line may not adequately describe the relationship between x and y outside the experimental region.

4. If $\hat{\rho} = 1$, the observed points all lie on the fitted line having a positive slope. If $\hat{\rho} = -1$, the observed points all lie on the fitted line having a negative slope.

5. a. $\hat{y} = 7.0 + 15.4x$. b. Reject $H_0: \beta_1 = 0$, since $t = 16.7$. c. $13.6 < \beta_1 < 17.2$. d. $\hat{\rho}^2 = .979$. (See exercise 2d.)

6. a. $\hat{y} = 6.96 + 2.31x$. c. $s^2 = .1219$. d. Reject $H_0: \beta_1 = 0$, since $t = 19.25$. e. $\hat{\rho} = .99$. f. $\hat{\rho}^2 = .979$. g. 9.27.

7. a. $\hat{y} = 20.47 - .76x$. b. $s^2 = .5822$. c. Reject H_0; $t = -22.3$. d. $-.86 < \beta_1 < -.66$. e. 9.83. f. $\hat{\rho}^2 = .984$ (See exercise 2d).

8. a. $\hat{y} = 95.6 - 1.275x$. c. Reject $H_0: \beta_1 = 0$, since $t = -4.98$. d. 65. e. $\hat{\rho} = -.87$; reject $H_0: \rho = 0$ since $t = -4.98$.

Chapter 11

1. Sample size; experimental variation.
2. Approximately 256.
3. Approximately 100.
4. Approximately 100.
5. Do not reject H_0; $t = 2.29$.
6. 1.11 ± 1.62.
7. Approximately 400.
8. Do not reject H_0; $t = 1.48$.
9. Approximately 40,000.
10. Approximately 41.
11. Reject H_0; $t = 2.97$; yes.

Chapter 12

1. Do not reject H_0; $F = 3.58$. Assumption has been met.
2. Do not reject H_0; $F = 2.38$; no.
3. a. 4.19. b. 11.26. c. 4.95. d. 4.32. e. 1.84.
4. Do not reject H_0; $F = 1.796$.
5. Reject H_0; $F = 2.06$.
6. Do not reject H_0; $F = 1.96$.
7. Do not reject H_0; $F = 2.14$.

Chapter 13

1. No; $F = 12.5834/4.8611 = 2.59$.
2. Yes; $F = 12908.74/2911.65 = 4.43$.
3. No; $F = 350.89/199.86 = 1.76$.
4. a. Reject H_0; $t = 3.199$. b. Reject H_0; $F = 547.6/53.5 = 10.24$. c. $t^2 = F$.
5. Reject H_0; $F = 126.07/10.23 = 12.32$.
6. Do not reject H_0; $F = .64$.

Chapter 14

1. Reject H_0; $X^2 = 7.97$.
2. Do not reject H_0; $X^2 = 1.709$.
3. Reject H_0; $X^2 = 9.333$.
4. Do not reject H_0; $X^2 = 3.673$.
5. Do not reject H_0; $X^2 = 8.727$.
6. Reject H_0; $X^2 = 25.63$.

Chapter 15

1. Sign test: related; Wilcoxon signed-rank: related; Wilcoxon rank-sum: independent.
2. $z = -2.54$. Reject H_0.
3. $T = 63$; with $\alpha = .05$ reject H_0 if $T \leqslant 101$. Reject H_0.
4. $\hat{\rho}_s = 1$. While $\rho = 1$ only when the data points all lie on the same straight line, ρ_s will be 1 whenever y increases steadily with x.
5. a. $\hat{\rho}_s = .8545$. b. $z = 2.56$; reject H_0; yes.
6. Reject H_0; $z = (T - \mu_T)/\sigma_T = -1.88$.
7. Do not reject H_0; $z = .90$.
8. Reject H_0 if $T \leqslant 11$; $T = 10$; reject H_0.
9. Reject H_0; $z = -2.11$.